THE AMERICAN EXPLORATION AND TRAVEL SERIES

# FOR SCIENCE AND NATIONAL GLORY

*The Spanish Scientific Expedition to America, 1862–1866*

University of Oklahoma Press : Norman

# FOR SCIENCE AND NATIONAL GLORY

The Spanish Scientific Expedition to America, 1862-1866

By ROBERT RYAL MILLER

*The paper on which this book is printed bears the watermark of the University of Oklahoma Press and has an effective life of at least three hundred years.*

500.9
M 61 f
66139
June 1969

*For Penny*

# Preface

SPANISH MONARCHS sponsored scientific expeditions to the New World over a period of four centuries, but the last great reconnaissance was in the 1860's when a royal scientific commission visited a dozen countries of Latin America. Although the naturalists crossed the Argentine Pampas, surveyed the Atacama Desert, examined Andean archaeological sites, photographed people and places from Brazil to California, descended the full length of the Amazon River, and sent home crates containing 82,000 specimens of plants, animals, and minerals, the story of their adventure is virtually unknown. There is no published account of it in English, French, or German, and the two printed summaries in Spanish are rare and not well known. Paucity of publicity about the journey is partly explained by Spanish political intrigues that affected the group and partly by tropical diseases that felled several of the naturalists before they had an opportunity to publish their findings.

Based on archival research in Spain and Latin America, this volume relates the curious story of the Spanish scientific expedition of 1862–66, officially termed the "Scientific Commission of the Pacific." In addition to governmental records, such as ships' logs and ministerial correspondence, sources include letters and original diaries of three of the naturalists, as well as 140 glass-plate photographs exposed by the official artist with the expedition. The tale itself is full of pathos and humor, with the inevitable personality clashes, enlivened in this case by a cleavage between naval officers and scientists.

More than a story of plant hunting and netting butterflies in the Amazon Basin, this account embraces the history of Spain and her relations with Latin America in the 1860's. What started out as a scientific expedition ended in war between Spain and four of her former colonies. United States history is also involved, since the Spanish resurgence in America occurred at a time when the Civil War precluded enforcement of the Monroe Doctrine. Although this book deals with the past, there are universal themes with particular relevance today—the role of government in scientific research, for example. Thus the work should appeal to a wide range of readers, whether their interests are science, history, Latin America, or adventure.

For financial assistance I wish to thank the Research Center of New Mexico State University and gratefully acknowledge the travel grant received from the Penrose Fund of the American Philosophical Society. Thanks are also due to officials and staff members of archives and libraries in Madrid, Spain—especially Captain Roberto Barreiro-Meiro of the Museo Naval, Emilio Fernández Galiano of the Jardín Botánico, and Rafael Alvarado and Señorita María de los Angeles Calatayud of the Museo de Ciencias Naturales. Except for two items, all the photographs were provided through the courtesy of the latter institution. Illustrations of the two Spanish ships came from the Museo Naval. George Hammond, former director of Bancroft Library at the University of California, was helpful in obtaining copies of the Spanish photographs. In Lima, Peru, Señorita Graciela Sánchez Cerro kindly made available newspapers, rare books, and manuscripts of the Biblioteca Nacional. Credit for the maps goes to Mrs. Adrienne Morgan, cartographer at the University of California; and I am grateful to Professors James King and Engel Sluiter of that university for their interest and advice. For his counsel and friendly encouragement, I am indebted to Lawrence Kinnaird, professor of history, emeritus, of the University of California.

Robert Ryal Miller

*University Park, N. M.*
*March 27, 1968*

# Contents

# Illustrations

## MAPS

FOR SCIENCE AND NATIONAL GLORY

*The Spanish Scientific Expedition to America, 1862–1866*

Abbreviations Used in Footnotes

AMCN—Archivo del Museo de Ciencias Naturales, Madrid
JB—Jardín Botánico, Madrid
MN—Museo Naval, Madrid

# Background to the Expedition

Spain is not usually remembered for scientific achievements, but a close look at her accomplishments in America reveals a rich heritage of technical investigation and publication, especially in the field of natural history. From the discovery of the New World to the nineteenth century, Iberian savants traveled throughout the Western Hemisphere, making systematic observations, collecting specimens and data, and formulating hypotheses. In addition to private or ecclesiastical scholars there were individuals and groups sent to America on scientific missions by Spanish kings and queens.

A long line of Spanish scientific voyages to America begins with Columbus and ends with the expedition of 1862–66. Any compilation would depend on one's definition of terms, but certainly hundreds of Spaniards qualify as scientific explorers of the New World. Some were sent to study flora and fauna of a particular viceroyalty, a few did research on native drugs, diseases, and cures, and a great number were ethnologists, tracking and cracking aboriginal languages and recording customs of the American Indians. Surveying the lands, charting the seas, and examining the resources of the Western Hemisphere, other Spaniards carried out official projects for their government. A summary of significant scientific exploration in America will set the stage for the nineteenth-century expedition.

Sixteenth-century American history is high-lighted by *conquistadores*, but there were also Spanish scholars in the New World. Gonzalo Fernández de Oviedo y Valdés (1478–1557), appointed "Chronicler of the Indies" by the king, also served many years as governor of Cartagena and Santo Domingo. Between 1514 and 1545, Oviedo crossed the Atlantic sixteen times, and he knew personally Balboa, Cortés, and Pizarro. He is best remembered for compiling a twenty-one-volume encyclopedia of American natural history and ethnology, the first part published in Spain in 1535.[1] His detailed descriptions of trees, plants, and herbs earned him the title "First Naturalist of the New World."

In 1570, King Philip II sent his court physician, Francisco Hernández (1514–78), to America as *protomédico*, or medical examiner, charged with studying useful plants and medicines. For six years he traveled around Mexico studying plants, questioning native physicians and pharmacists, and compiling six folio volumes of text and ten of drawings illustrating what he had observed. Failing in health, he decided against a similar undertaking in Peru and returned to Spain with a large collection of birds, insects, fish, reptiles, seeds, and live plants. Hernández died in 1578, and only part of his great thesaurus was published a generation later. Although his original manuscript was destroyed in a fire in the Escorial Palace in 1671, a copy of the text was later discovered and printed.[2]

Spanish missionaries working in America in the sixteenth and seventeenth centuries assembled a storehouse of natural history and anthropological information. Franciscan Friar Bernardino Sahagún (1499?–1590), with the help of Aztec princes, compiled a monumental work about pre-Cortesian Mexico. His information on the Indians covers their history, religious beliefs and practices, weapons, myths, music, oral literature, agricultural methods, arts and crafts, costumes, and other valuable data utilized by his contemporaries and later generations. Sahagún wrote his manuscripts in both Castilian and Nahuatl. Only the Spanish version was censored by the Inquisition, his unexpurgated observations being preserved for future scholars.[3]

[1] Gonzalo Fernández de Oviedo y Valdés, *La historia general de las Indias; primera parte de la historia natural*, and first complete edition *Historia general y natural de las Indias* . . . .

[2] Francisco Hernández, *Nova plantarvm, animalivm et mineralivm mexicanorvm*. See also [Hernández] *Obras completas* (ed. by Germán Somolinos d'Ardois).

[3] Fray Bernardino Sahagún, *Historia general de las cosas de Nueva España* (ed. by Carlos María Bustamante); *Florentine Codex; General History of the Things of New Spain* (trans. by Charles Dibble and Arthur Anderson).

*Itinerary map of Spanish scientific expedition, 1862–1866*

The Jesuit Father Bernabé Cobo (1582–1657) spent more than fifty years studying plant and animal life in Peru, Mexico, and the Caribbean. The fruit of his investigations was embodied in a manuscript of forty-three books, of which only ten have been located. These were discovered in the Spanish archives by Marcos Jiménez de la Espada, a member of the scientific expedition of 1862, who edited and published Cobo's writings almost three hundred years after they were written.[4] Sahagún and Cobo represent a multitude of priest-naturalists working in America. One could add other names like Simón Rojas, Humberto Coronado, and Pedro Ordóñez y Ceballos.

Eighteenth-century Spain followed Europe in an awakened interest in natural history. An international scholarly debate over the size and shape of the earth prompted the French Academy of Sciences to sponsor an expedition which would measure an arc of latitude at the Equator near Quito in the viceroyalty of Peru. In 1735 mathematician and geodesist Charles Marie de la Condamine headed a group of a dozen scientists—including two young Spanish engineers, Jorge Juan and Antonio de Ulloa—who spent about ten years in South America on one of the most important scientific expeditions to that continent. Besides proving that the earth bulges at the Equator, La Condamine collected samples of quinine bark, curare, and rubber, then returned to France after descending the full length of the Amazon River, mapping it along the way.[5]

Ten years later a Swedish botanist led a Spanish scientific expedition to northern South America. Responding to a request from the Spanish monarch, in 1752 the great Swedish botanist Carl Linnaeus sent his protégé Pedro Loefling (1729–56), to Spain, where he botanized for two years before sailing for Venezuela. He and his group remained in the Guiana jungle compiling a *Flora Cumanensis* from 1754 until 1756, when Loefling died of a tropical fever. About

[4] Bernabé Cobo, *Historia del Nuevo Mundo* (ed. by Marcos Jiménez de la Espada).

[5] La Condamine published half a dozen books about his American travels; the major one was *Relation abrégée d'un voyage fait dans l'intérieur de l'Amérique Méridionale.*

1,700 folio pages of his valuable notes and drawings were taken to Madrid where they still repose in the Botanical Garden. Some of Loefling's American notes and correspondence were published by Linnaeus, and a recent monograph published in Spain covers the Venezuelan trip.[6]

Spanish botanists Hipólito Ruíz and José Pavón earned international reputations for their decade of travels and studies in Peru, Chile, and Ecuador. When they returned to Spain in 1788, they brought with them twenty-nine boxes with herbariums and drawings, as well as more than a hundred live plants for the Botanical Garden. Unfortunately, their main collection of fifty-three crates with eight hundred drawings, dried plants, seeds, resins, balsams, and minerals was lost when the ship carrying them was wrecked off the coast of Portugal. Ruíz and Pavón published their *Prodromus* in Madrid in 1794 and three volumes of *Flora Peruviana et Chilensis* a few years later.[7]

Meanwhile, José Celestino Mutis (1732–1808) headed a royal botanical expedition in New Granada. Appointed in 1783, the Spanish physician and his assistants first established a botanical garden in Quito, then in 1791 moved their headquarters to Bogotá. Personnel varied from year to year, but there were often fifteen or twenty botanists and artists collecting, describing, and illustrating plants of the viceroyalty. Mutis died in Bogotá in 1808, and the expedition ended a few years later when New Granada became independent from Spain. Eleven volumes of text and almost 7,000 botanical plates were sent to Madrid along with 124 crates of seeds, wood specimens, minerals, and a herbarium of 20,000 plants. This marvelous collection remained unpublished until recently, when the governments of Spain and Colombia initiated a joint effort to print fifty-one volumes of the *Flora . . . del Nuevo Reino de Granada*.[8]

[6] Carl Linnaeus, *Iter Hispanicum, eller Resa til spanska Länderna uti Europa och America* . . . . Stig Rydén, *Pedro Loefling en Venezuela* (*1754–1756*).

[7] The labors and writings of Ruíz and Pavón are well presented in Arthur Robert Steele, *Flowers for the King; the Expedition of Ruíz and Pavón and the Flora of Peru.*

[8] [José Celestino Mutis,] *Flora de la Real Expedición Botánica del Nuevo Reino de Granada.*

The Royal Botanical Expedition to New Spain, 1787–96, was a part of the scientific resurgence of Enlightened Spain. Martín de Sessé y Lacasta, a Spanish physician, led the group of naturalists and artists, who collected and analyzed plants from Vancouver Island to Guatemala, inclusive. A Mexican botanist, José Mariano Moziño, joined the expedition and proved to be one of the most able members. Sessé and Moziño arrived in Spain in 1803 with a large herbarium and 1,400 expertly prepared botanical plates, but the Napoleonic wars prevented publication of the material. Finally, almost a century later, the texts of *Flora Mexicana* and *Plantae Novae Hispaniae* were published in Mexico without the illustrations.[9]

Stimulated by the famous voyages of Captain James Cook and Louis Bougainville, the Spanish government authorized a "round-the-world" scientific expedition headed by Captain Alejandro Malaspina. From 1789 to 1795 his ships, *Descubierta* and *Atrevida*, carrying naturalists Antonio Pineda, Louis Née, and Tadeo Haenke, visited American ports from Patagonia to Nootka Sound. Pineda spent eight fruitful months in Mexico, while the rest of the group sailed to California and back. Later the ships crossed the Pacific to Guam, the Philippines, New Zealand, and the Fiji Islands, returning to South America and finally to Spain. Malaspina's subsequent romantic involvement with Queen María Luisa of Spain led to his exile and a ban on publishing the expedition's findings. The Malaspina manuscripts, like the others—from Hernández to Mutis—were neglected for years but eventually some of them were printed.[10]

At the turn of the nineteenth century, when the use of vaccine to immunize against smallpox was newly discovered, the Spanish government sent the Balmis expedition to the New World with medical teams, who penetrated mountains and jungles vaccinating American Indians by the thousands.[11] But this was Spain's penulti-

[9] Harold William Rickett, "The Royal Botanical Expedition to New Spain," *Chronica Botanica*, Vol. XI, No. 1 (1947), 1–82.

[10] Pedro de Novo y Colson, *Viaje político-científico alrededor del mundo por las corbetas* Descubierta *y* Atrevida.

[11] Gonzalo Díaz de Iraola, *La vuelta al mundo de la expedición de la vacuna.*

mate scientific voyage; foreign and domestic crises precluded others for fifty years.

Scientists from England, France, Germany, and the United States were the principal explorers of Latin America in the first half of the nineteenth century. When the Spanish colonies became independent republics, thousands of foreign traders, travelers, and soldiers of fortune visited the area. In addition, hundreds of physical and natural scientists with specialties from anthropology to zoology began to climb the volcanoes and descend the arroyos in search of exotic specimens unique to the Western Hemisphere. Some, like Charles Darwin, Alexander von Humboldt, and Matthew Fontaine Maury, postulated theories based on their American observations; others had more limited goals and accomplishments. Prince Maximilian von Wied-Neuwied wanted to explore the east coast of Brazil; Lieutenant James Gilliss, United States Navy, journeyed to Chile to observe a lunar eclipse and astronomical phenomena; and English artist Frederick Catherwood executed architectural drawings of Mayan temples in Central America.[12] By mid-century an awakened interest in the scientific resources of America was felt in Spain.

But the nineteenth century was disastrous for Spain: Her decline involved loss of empire, financial chaos, years of civil war, public and private immorality on the part of the Queen, and extraordinary political instability. For decades the country was really in the hands of two generals, Ramón Narváez and Leopoldo O'Dónnell, who alternated as prime minister. To draw attention from the worsening domestic situation, General O'Dónnell committed the armed forces to a series of overseas ventures, which were unsuccessful but which fanned patriotism at home and kept him in power.

Ultramarine military operations began in 1858 when Spanish soldiers from the Philippine Islands joined French forces in a four-

---

[12] Prinz Maximilian von Wied-Neuwied, *Travels in Brazil in 1815, 1816, and 1817*. Lt. James Gilliss, U.S.N., *Observations to Determine the Solar Parallax*, Vol. III of *U.S. Naval Astronomical Expedition to the Southern Hemisphere During the Years 1849–'50–'51–'52*.

year armed intervention in Vietnam. Spain gained no honor and few concessions from this campaign, while France strengthened her position in the Far East. An appraisal of the war by a Spanish military historian concludes, "Once more the spirit of Don Quixote accompanied us in this engagement in Indochina."[13]

In 1859, O'Dónnell, the quixotic general-politician, personally led Spanish troops in a six months' war against the Moors of North Africa. This latter-day crusade against her ancient foes was popular with the masses in Spain, but it cost seven thousand Iberian lives and resulted in no territorial gain or other adequate compensation.

Spain's attempt to reassert her power in America began in the 1860's when the Civil War in the United States precluded enforcement of the Monroe Doctrine. First the Dominican Republic was reannexed, the land and people reverting to colonial status in 1861. For four years Spain tried to enforce her law and order on that Caribbean island, finally abandoning the venture after the loss of ten thousand soldiers and the expenditure of huge sums of money.

Meanwhile, O'Dónnell agreed to join French and English military intervention in Mexico, Spanish troops being the first to land in December, 1861. It soon became apparent that France intended to control the ancient Aztec kingdom, whereupon the English and Spanish forces withdrew. Spain gained nothing but the hostility of Latin-American republics from the chimerical campaign.

War with four Pacific republics of South America climaxed the cycle of Spanish military escapades in America. Seizure of the Chincha Islands off the coast of Peru by Spanish ships in 1864 initiated hostilities which were followed by bombardment of the ports of Valparaíso, Chile, and Callao, Peru. Active combat ended in 1866, when the Spanish fleet sailed for home, and an armistice was agreed upon in 1871; but peace treaties were not concluded with the American allies until 1885.

Spain's war with the Pacific republics engulfed the scientific expedition accompanying the warships to America; in fact, it is impossible

[13] General Emilio Esteban-Infantes y Martín, *Expediciones españolas, siglo XIX,* 240.

to talk about one without mentioning the other. Several writers, notably from Peru or Chile, maintain that the scientific commission was only a screen used to camouflage premeditated military aggression,[14] but it appears that the two groups were thrown together at the last moment more as a matter of economic expediency than of subterfuge. Since there are good published accounts of the war, including an excellent book in English,[15] the present work will concentrate on the scientific expedition—its origins and accomplishments.

[14] Gustavo Pons Muzzo, *Historia del conflicto entre el Perú y España, 1864–1866*, 36; Joaquín Edwards Bello, *El bombardeo de Valparaíso y su época*, 12.

[15] William Columbus Davis, *The Last Conquistadores: The Spanish Intervention in Peru and Chile, 1863–1866*. Pedro de Novo y Colson, *Historia de la guerra de España en el Pacífico*.

# II

# Organizing the Scientific Commission

Proposals to send a group of Spanish naturalists to America to acquire scientific data and specimens began about 1860. At that time scholars were pointing out that national museums and universities lacked examples of basic New World items like buffalo, llama, rhea, condor, redwood trees, pampa grass, volcanic ash, and mineral specimens. Nor were there artifacts from the American Indian civilizations—the feathered headdresses, golden goblets, and hieroglyphic books forwarded to Spain in earlier centuries had gravitated to museums in Vienna, Paris, London, or private European collections. The idea of a new scientific reconnaissance of Spain's former colonies appeared intermittently in Spanish newspaper articles and was discussed in official circles. Notes about the matter passed between the minister of public works, Marqués de la Vega Armijo, and the director of public instruction, Pedro Sabau, while subordinate correspondence involved leaders of Madrid's Botanical Garden and Museum of Natural Science. By May, 1862, meetings were being held to make definite plans and choose personnel for the proposed expedition.[1]

Meanwhile, beginning in the spring of 1860 the ministers of state and navy were planning to send a squadron of ships on a good-will visit to the Pacific Coast of America.[2] Divers reasons could justify such an action, but the compelling ones were political. Although they had been independent for a generation, several of Spain's former colonies still harbored a grudge against her. In the case of Peru no

---

[1] Pedro Sabau to Miguel Colmeiro, May 26, 1862, Colmeiro Corresp., 5 Div., Nos. 26, 60, Jardín Botánico, Madrid (JB).

[2] Agustín Jesús Barreiro, *Historia de la Comisión Científica del Pacífico, 1862 a 1865*, 40.

treaty had been signed whereby Spain recognized the independence of that republic. A visit by the royal fleet would also boost the morale of the considerable number of Spanish citizens residing in Latin America, many of them businessmen.

Following a two-year delay caused by other foreign commitments and engagements, the Pacific expedition was finally organized in the spring and summer of 1862. The navy minister appointed Rear Admiral Luis H. Pinzón to command the squadron composed of the frigates *Resolución* and *Triunfo* and the schooner *Covadonga*. The last, already in American waters, was ordered to rendezvous with the frigates in Buenos Aires. All three ships were wooden sailing vessels with auxiliary steam engines. It is interesting to note that the Spanish Navy at this time consisted of nine frigates, a number of schooners, and a few other ships under construction.[3]

By the end of May, 1862, the Spanish government had decided to incorporate the scientific expedition into the projected naval goodwill visit. A communiqué from the director of public instruction illustrates this point:

> A squadron under Admiral Pinzón being destined for the Pacific, it is advantageous that a scientific mission accompany it as cultured nations do in similar circumstances and as Spain did with great distinction in the second half of the last century . . . this office submits two bases regarding the project of so much interest for the advancement of science and national glory.[4]

The memorandum then outlined the procedure for budgeting the expedition and named an eight-man advisory committee to draw up detailed plans, including selection of personnel and equipment for the voyage. In addition to the director of public instruction, committee members included the dean of the College of Science at the University of Madrid and officials of the Botanical Garden, Planetarium, and Museum of Natural Science.

In subsequent meetings the committee formulated basic objectives

[3] List of warships in Novo y Colson, *Historia*, 84.
[4] Director of public instruction to minister of public works, May 27, 1862, Barreiro, *Historia*, 41–42.

for the mission, officially designated the Scientific Commission of the Pacific. Responsibility for astronomical and geographical observations went to the naval officers of the squadron, while the civilian scientists were charged with two major tasks:

> To gather facts and information in order to resolve some outstanding scientific problems, and to collect plants, animals, and other objects of nature in order to enrich our collections with new species, and to aid in the propagation and acclimatization of others useful to the life of man and beneficial to applied science.[5]

Choosing scientists for the expedition was the most difficult task for the advisory committee. Some who were nominated withdrew because of family objections, others gave poor health as a reason, while a few felt they could not leave their work or positions in Spain. Finally, eight men were selected and agreed to serve on the Scientific Commission of the Pacific.

Patricio María Paz y Membiela, a retired naval captain and naturalist, headed the commission. He was given the title of president and an annual salary of 15,000 pesetas. This seemed like an ideal choice; for Paz, who was fifty-five years old, had had a distinguished career in the royal navy and was respected as a conchologist, specializing in mollusks. While visiting ports around the world, he had assembled an extraordinary collection of shells, numbering over 40,000 and representing some 12,000 species. For the American expedition Paz was expected to be an administrator, send monthly activity and financial reports, and do investigation and collecting in his special area. As it turned out, Paz was a poor choice, for he was partially deaf, had an irascible personality, and quarreled frequently with the ship's officers and other members of the expedition. The situation got so bad that after a year in America he resigned and returned to Spain. Nevertheless, for his service as president of the commission, Paz was later awarded the Cross of Isabella the Catholic.[6]

A professor of natural science was appointed second in command

[5] *Ibid.*, 42–43.

[6] Paz's shell collection is now in Madrid's Museo de Ciencias Naturales. Marcos Jiménez de la Espada, "*Nota biográfica, Patricio María Paz y Membiela,*" *Actas de*

of the overseas commission. He was Fernando Amor y Mayor, born in Madrid in 1820 and a graduate of the central university, where he received a doctorate in pharmacy in 1845. Amor taught chemistry, physics, and natural history in the Institutes of Cuenca, Córdoba, and Valladolid before joining the expedition. His notable collections of minerals, beetles, and flowering plants kept him in contact with professors in Madrid as well as with well-known French scientists. A member of several professional societies, delegate to international congresses, and recipient of medals for his scientific entries in London and Paris expositions, Amor had excellent qualifications and a strong desire to participate in the expedition to America. His annual salary was fixed at 9,600 pesetas, and he was assigned the geological and etymological fields for his area of competence and his collection. As will be noted later, his brilliant work was cut short by death from a liver infection contracted in South America. Until his mortal illness Amor kept a daily journal, but most of it was lost in a fire aboard one of the Spanish ships. As a lasting monument to this Spanish scientific martyr, some eight biological species, beginning with *Asida Amori* Pérez Arcas, bear his name.[7]

Francisco de Paula Martínez y Sáez, a young naturalist and professor at the University of Madrid, was the third man chosen for the expedition. In addition to his responsibilities related to collection of fish, aquatic mammals and reptiles, he served as secretary for the Pacific commission. His salary was stated as 7,600 pesetas, although he did not receive it regularly. Born in Spain's capital in 1835, Martínez became a pharmacist first, then earned a degree in natural science. On the expedition to America he collected about 30,000 specimens, sending them back to Spanish museums. He was a quiet, religious man and kept a detailed diary, with entries for almost every day. These volumes are valuable sources of information about the expedition. Other members of the group kept diaries too, but

la *Soc. Española de Hist. Nat.*, IV (1875), 24. "*Patricio María Paz y Membiela,*" *Enciclopedia universal ilustrada*, XLII, (Barcelona, 1920), 1104.

[7] Joaquín Olmedilla y Puig, *Elogio histórico de D. Fernando Amor y Mayor*. Barreiro, *Historia*, 434–40.

their notations generally dealt with scientific matters, while Martínez commented frankly on personalities, perplexities, and triumphs of the commission. After returning to Spain from America, Martínez taught in various Spanish universities and published some fifty scholarly articles, most of them in the journal of the Spanish Society of Natural History, an organization of which he was cofounder. He also published a textbook on vertebrate zoology and was coeditor of a large illustrated volume on the bivalve mollusks collected by Paz and others on the expedition to America. Martínez outlived all the other members of the commission and enjoyed good health until his death in 1908.[8]

By far the most outstanding member of the expedition was Marcos Jiménez de la Espada, a zoologist whose wide investigation brought him fame as a geographer, historian, and naturalist. He was born in Cartagena in 1831 and studied at the University of Madrid, where he stayed on—first as an assistant and finally as professor of natural history—for forty-three years. During the trip to America, Espada supervised the collection of mammals, birds, and reptiles, sending back to Europe for the first time live specimens of fauna, including Patagonian hare, guanaco, black-necked swan, condor, a wild turkey of Peru, and sixteen new species of frogs. In Peru he became deeply interested in the Inca Indian civilization. Upon his return to Spain he devoted many years to research and publication about pre-Columbian America. The Peruvian government later presented him with a gold medal honoring his historical studies in that region, and today his photograph hangs in a place of honor in the department of history at San Marcos University in Lima, Peru. Espada founded two important Spanish scientific organizations: one for natural history and the other a geographical society. Late in life he was nominated for membership in the Royal Academy of History, an honor he had to decline because he did not have the one thousand pesetas needed

[8] Francisco de Paula Martínez y Sáez, *"Diario,"* Archivo del Museo de Ciencias Naturales, Madrid (AMCN), hereafter cited as Martínez, *"Diario."* J. Gorgoza, *"Datos biográficos del profesor D. Fco. de Paula Martínez Sáez,"* Boletín de la Soc. Española de Hist. Nat., Vol. VIII (1908), 208.

to publish an entry manuscript and to buy the required vestment. Espada's many publications range from technical articles on amphibians of the Napo River to histories of America—written by sixteenth-century chroniclers—which he edited. Part of the diary he kept during the American expedition was published posthumously.[9]

The anthropologist-ethnologist of the group was a Spaniard from Cuba named Manuel Almagro y Vega. Born in Matanzas, Cuba, in 1834, he enrolled in the medical school of Havana University in 1850, transferred the following year to the University of Madrid, and three years later entered the Sorbonne in Paris. During his eight years in France he studied medicine and physical anthropology, joining the Anthropological Society of Paris. In 1862, having received his diploma and title of medical doctor, he returned to Madrid, where he continued advanced medical courses while having his physician's license revalidated in Spain. Almagro next sought and received a commission in the medical corps of the royal army, his station to be in Cuba; but appointment as anthropologist with the scientific expedition took precedence over his military assignment. He sailed from Cádiz on August 10, 1862, leaving his young bride behind. Almagro was one of the first trained professional anthropologists to do field work in America, where he excavated archaeological sites and studied aboriginal life from Patagonia to Panama. He was responsible for sending hundreds of Indian artifacts to Spain, along with skulls, skeletons, and mummies. Almagro was the official historian of the scientific commission, but he never did complete his projected multivolume history of the expedition, and his voluminous notes disappeared long ago. He did publish a short summary of the

[9] Marcos Jiménez de la Espada, *Diario de la expedición al Pacífico llevado a cabo por una comisión de naturalistas españoles durante los años 1862–1865*, (ed. by Agustín Jesús Barreiro). Cesáreo Fernández Duro, *El Doctor D. Marcos Jiménez de la Espada, naturalista, geógrafo é historiador; necrología*. Francisco de Paula Martínez y Sáez, *El Doctor D. Marcos Jiménez de la Espada, zoólogo y viajero naturalista, nota biográfica*. The two preceding items also appear in *Bol. de la Soc. Geográfica de Madrid*, Vol. XL. Agustín Jesús Barreiro, *Biografía de D. Marcos Jiménez de la Espada, 1831–1898*. "Marcos Jiménez de la Espada," *Enciclopedia universal ilustrada*, XXVIII, 2788.

trip in 1866, noting in the preface that "it was difficult to write a book of small proportions and popular style in less than two months, describing half a world in a few chapters, numerous observations in a few pages, the sublimeness of American nature in a few lines."[10] Almagro returned to Havana in 1866, where he remained the last dozen years of his life.

Probably the most diligent member of the expedition was botanist Juan Isern y Batlló, whose extensive herbaria and plant descriptions from the New World are now in the Botanical Garden in Madrid. Isern, who was born in the province of Gerona near the French border, began collecting plants as a youth, later collecting and selling them to support his studies at the University of Barcelona. In 1851 he took a post in Madrid at the Botanical Garden, continuing his excursions in the countryside to gather plant specimens. He was thirty-six years old and had a wife and two children, a third expected, when he joined the expedition to America. Some of his letters from South America sent to friends in Spain were published in a Madrid periodical; others are in the archives of the Botanical Garden. In one he noted that he was collecting stalks, fruits, seeds, and bulbs, representing "many new species and probably some new genera." His observations on the difficulty of collecting specimens in the New World are interesting:

> Those who have not visited America believe that it is very easy to form great collections in a short time; the opposite [is true]. . . . In America everything is large. The highest mountains of Europe are pygmies compared with peaks of the Andes. Consequently the species are more spread out and the naturalist traveler must cover much more terrain in order to encounter an equal number of them.[11]

Isern's tramps across Argentina, Chile, Peru, Bolivia, and Ecuador,

[10] Manuel de Almagro, *Breve descripción de los viajes hechos en América por la Comisión científica enviada por S.M.C. durante los años 1862 a 1866.* "Manuel de Almagro y Vega," *Enciclopedia universal ilustrada,* IV, [1910?], 788. Barreiro, *Historia,* 449–52.

[11] Isern to Laureano Pérez Arcas, Quito, Ecuador, Jan. 21, 1865, excerpts in Barreiro, *Historia,* 491–93; other letters in *El Pabellón Médico,* Madrid, III, No. 113, 451–52; IV, No. 125, 26–27.

and a voyage down the Amazon are reflected in the 8,000 plants he sent back to Spain, all carefully prepared and labeled. Unfortunately, the botanist picked up a tropical infection in Brazil and died in January, 1866, shortly after returning to Madrid.[12]

The last two men of the scientific commission were auxiliary members—a taxidermist and an artist-photographer. Little is known about either of them, and both quit the expedition, returning separately to Spain. The first was a medical doctor, Bartolomé Puig de Galup, an assistant taxidermist at the University of Barcelona in 1862. His technical work on the voyage was, according to Marcos Jiménez de la Espada, "scanty and of poor quality." Doctor Puig met and married a Chilean girl and stayed for several years in her country before finally returning to Spain.[13] The expedition's photographer, Rafael de Castro y Ordóñez, exposed some three hundred glass plates in America. Good prints of about half of them are in the archives of Madrid's Museum of Natural Science. Castro died soon after returning to Spain; whereupon his brother and other photographers continued the work of making twenty sets of prints from the negatives.[14] Although it is known that Castro made sketches and illustrated biological specimens for the expedition, none of these have been published or located.

By midsummer of 1862 members of the scientific commission had been selected, and news of the expedition appeared in Spanish newspapers. Considering Spain's recent interventions in Mexico and the Dominican Republic, it was not strange that some Latin-American countries reacted with fear when they heard of the proposed naval-scientific mission. The Peruvian government contemplated building additional warships and fortifying harbors, and sent an agent to Buenos Aires to intercept Admiral Pinzón to question him about the purposes of the visit. Perhaps Peruvians were justified in their attitude, for a series of articles in Spanish newspapers, beginning in June,

[12] "Juan Isern y Batlló," *Enciclopedia universal ilustrada*, XXVIII (Barcelona, 1926), 2058. Barreiro, *Historia*, 474–94.

[13] Puig's thesis, *De la moral en el médico*.

[14] Mariano Paz Graells Corresp., Archivo, Museo de Ciencias Naturales, Madrid (AMCN).

1861, called for Spanish occupation of the rich guano islands off the coast of Peru, "property which never has ceased belonging to our country," according to one editorial.[15]

But the Spanish government, supported by administration newspapers, maintained that the expedition had no hostile intentions—that its purposes were to extend good will and further science.

> Apart from the moral and material interests of Spain, this naval expedition will be no less fruitful for science . . . . We see that a Peruvian newspaper is alarmed by the dispatch of this small expedition . . . these few boats are not going with a motive of conquest, but yes, they will conquer . . . data for science and brotherly permanent friendship . . . . If they will make another type of conquest . . . it will not be the Spaniards who will decide, nor Peruvian men, but the beautiful Peruvian women.[16]

Before leaving Spain, Admiral Pinzón received orders from both the minister of navy and the minister of state. The former specified ports to be visited from Pernambuco, Brazil, to Río de la Plata, then around Cape Horn to Valparaíso, Chile, Callao, Peru, Acapulco, Mexico, and Alta California. On days when the American republics celebrated their victorious battles and independence from Spain, the squadron was to put out to sea to avoid any trouble.[17]

Instructions from the Spanish minister of state reminded Pinzón that in each republic there were representatives of the Queen with whom he should confer and whose decisions he should support. It was stated that the Spanish government would not consent to any violence perpetrated against its subjects, and in case of some affront affecting Spanish interests, the naval chief should assist in bringing about an immediate reparation. Peru was signaled as being "one of the republics most hostile to Spain"; therefore the Spanish force should display itself more in ports of that country.[18]

[15] *La América*, June 24, 1861, 5. See also *La España*, June 12, 18, 1861; José de Couto, *Cuestiones de Méjico, Venezuela y América en general*; Novo y Colson, *Historia*, 89; Mark Van Aken, *Pan-Hispanism; Its Origin and Development to 1866*, 107.

[16] *La América*, June 24, 1862, 15.

[17] Novo y Colson, *Historia*, 88.     [18] *Ibid.*, 86–88.

Finally, in August, 1862, the naval units and scientists rendez-voused in the Atlantic port of Cádiz prior to their departure. The squadron was composed of two wooden frigates, *Resolución* and *Nuestra Señora del Triunfo*, similar three-masted sailing ships with auxiliary steam engines primarily used for docking and in calms. Admiral Pinzón chose the *Resolución*, captained by Manuel de la Rígada, as his flagship. Captain Enrique Croquer y Pavía commanded the other vessel. Displacing 2,940 tons and equipped with forty-two cannons, the *Triunfo* was 243 feet long and 48 feet wide amidships. Personnel aboard totaled 483 men, including 11 naval cadets, 2 physicians, a chaplain, and the civilian scientists.[19]

Four staterooms on the battery deck of the *Triunfo* were set aside for the commission, as well as two additional compartments below decks for storage of their equipment and collections. Paz shared the captain's quarters; Amor and Martínez had a large stateroom about twelve by seventeen feet; Espada and Puig were in a similar one; Isern and Almagro's room was about four feet shorter, as was Castro's combination bedroom-darkroom. It should be added that in each of these rooms was a cannon which took up considerable space. In one of Espada's letters he listed and described the furniture: a combination commode-desk with a bookcase on top, an iron bed "like those used in homes," a marble wash basin, two or three chairs, rug, drapes, and the promise of a table, space permitting.[20]

Just before leaving Spain, the president of the scientific commission called a meeting of his group to explain the rules under which they would operate on the voyage. Paz was a principal author of the "official regulations" drafted in Madrid and approved by the minister of public works on July 9, 1862. The nineteen articles of this document spell out the purposes, delineate the work, and define the obligations of the commission. One section divided the members into first and second categories, then ranked them on a descending scale of importance from president to photographer. Another article specified:

[19] Roster of *Triunfo* crew tipped in at beginning of Martínez, *"Diario,"* AMCN.
[20] Espada to Mariano Paz Graells, Cádiz, July 30, 1862, Barreiro, *Historia*, 503.

Each of the individuals charged with collecting will carry a book in which to record excursions made, who accompanied him, and what specimens were collected. He will assign numbers to the objects .... After each number, comments worthy of mention ... as the common name, any special use made, its coloration, whether it is perishable, its abundance, scarcity, season, etc.[21]

Other articles dealt with financial reports and forwarding specimens to Spain.

Several of the scientists complained about the regulations, saying they would not have agreed to go on the trip if they had known the terms. Espada wrote a long letter to the head of the museum in which he recounted stormy protest sessions and contradictory statements of their leader. He particularly objected to the division of reptiles and mammals into aquatic and terrestrial, saying it was "absurd and impractical."[22] But it was too late to back down, so Espada and the others boarded the *Triunfo*, hoping that along the way some amendments could be made to the official rules.

[21] *Reglamento*, in Barreiro, *Historia*, 499–501; English trans. in Appendix A, below.

[22] Espada to Paz Graells, Cádiz, July 30, 1862, Barreiro, *Historia*, 504–505.

# III

# Atlantic Ocean Islands

Tʜᴇ sᴄɪᴇɴᴛɪꜰɪᴄ and naval expedition left Cádiz, Spain, on August 10, 1862, and headed for South America, with two island stops on the way. Favorable winds and seas carried the ships to the Canary Islands, where they anchored at the capital city, Santa Cruz de Tenerife, on the fourteenth. Espada observed in his diary that the average speed had been about seven knots. Aboard ship some strange royal navy customs were noted by the landlubber civilians. One which Amor termed "abusive" was the requirement that all sailors purchase tobacco whether or not they used it. Aside from seasickness on the part of the scientists and the drowning of one of the crew members, the first part of the odyssey was uneventful.[1]

The seven Canary Islands, Spanish territory since their conquest in 1402 on behalf of the Crown of Castile, comprised some 29,000 square miles. The Guanches, who were in possession of the Canaries before the Spanish conquest, were Caucasians of gigantic stature and probably descendants of the Berber people, whose language they spoke. By the nineteenth century they had disappeared as a separate race but were commemorated in the capital's principal monument, composed of four statues representing the last aboriginal kings. Opposite this on the same plaza was a statue of Our Lady of Candelaria, erected by the Spanish conquerors in the fifteenth century. In the governor's mansion the visiting Spaniards examined three recently excavated Guanche mummies. The governor promised to send the relics to the Museum of Natural Sciences in Madrid. Four years

[1] Jiménez de la Espada, *Diario*, 6.

later Almagro complained that they had not yet arrived, but sometime later they did.[2]

Although in port for only two days, the Spanish naturalists managed to collect specimens of fish, mollusks, insects, and a herbarium of 437 examples. On an excursion inland to the old capital city of La Laguna they observed that the islanders used dromedaries as beasts of burden, and were told that there were wild camels in the interior, "hunted for the many uses that such an animal has."[3]

The scientists talked with various officials in the Canaries who gave them statistics on insular agricultural production, exports, and imports. They learned that their government had established a botanical garden in Santa Cruz de Tenerife, but that it was "rather neglected and decayed" and in need of restoration. They also heard of a Spanish proposal to create an acclimatization station in the Canaries, where plants and animals from tropical zones would be brought prior to their transfer to the Iberian Peninsula. Fernando Amor, the geologist-entomologist, was especially interested in this project and agreed to serve as director of it when he returned from the expedition to America. His death in 1863 made it impossible to carry out the plan.[4]

From the Canary Islands the expedition sailed southwest toward the Cape Verde Islands, where they arrived six days later, August 22. During the voyage they observed flying fish, turtles, phosphorescence in the sea, and a comet. Martínez' diary entry for August 17 describes a Sunday Mass aboard the *Triunfo*:

> The crew were in dress uniform—it was held in the open on deck. The altar was a table covered with white cloth and had two large candles; above the altar was a painting of Our Lady of Carmen. It was a grandiose spectacle, but I could only hear the voice of the priest and the noise of the water. The service ended with a cheer "Long Live the Queen!" given by the captain and echoed by everyone.

[2] Almagro, *Breve*, 9; Martínez, "*Diario*," Aug. 14–15, 1862, AMCN; Barreiro, *Historia*, 55.

[3] Martínez, "*Diario*," Aug. 14, 1862, AMCN.

[4] Barreiro, *Historia*, 55, quoting Amor's diary.

On another occasion Martínez, who was very devout, pointed out that the chaplain spent many hours giving religious instruction to the crew members, and that nothing was so moving as religious services at sea "which help the poor sailors to bear with patience the rude and dangerous work which they are continually doing."[5]

The Spanish ships were anchored in the Cape Verde Islands for three days, taking on coal brought there from England. Located about four hundred miles west of Cape Verde, Africa, the archipelago belonging to Portugal embraced nine inhabited islands and a number of uninhabited islets. Santo Antão, the largest and most fertile island, did not have a good harbor, so they put in at Porto Grande Bay, São Vicente Island.

Once ashore the scientists first visited the Spanish consul, then spread out to begin their work. Paz and Martínez went to the beach in search of mollusks and zoophytes and Amor to the edge of town pursuing insects, while Espada and Isern botanized on some near-by hills. Espada observed that the crater-shaped island was of volcanic origin with gray and black basaltic rocks covering the arid surface, and along the coast there were lodes of crystalized calcium carbonate interspersed with veins of basalt. There were no native trees on the island. There were, however, a few trees imported from Africa and America, such as the palm, banana, and *cherimoya*; and desert shrubs of the tamarisk family were quite common in the interior of the island. The Spaniards observed a few species of reptiles, but no mammals except for the human inhabitants. As there was little cultivatable land, most of the men worked in the dock area loading coal.[6]

According to Almagro, the population was made up of a few Portuguese government officials, even fewer English coal company employees, and about six hundred Portuguese-speaking Negroes of the Yolof tribe, related to those on the west coast of Africa. The Cape Verde islanders were Roman Catholic, and they had a small, "poorly decorated" church served by a Negro priest. Proof of the wretched

---

[5] Martínez, *"Diario,"* Aug. 17, 31, 1862, AMCN.

[6] Espada to Mariano Paz Graells, Rio de Janeiro, Nov. 2, 1862, Jiménez de la Espada, *Diario*, 10–11.

condition of the natives is found in several of the Spanish diaries. Espada, remarking on the number of Negroes who went about completely nude, said that when he saw the reflection of the sun on their colored skin, they reminded him of bronze statues. He called the women lascivious and covetous, noting that one of them even offered to sell him her young child. Amor said that the women were all of the poor class and that they were in general tall and robust. Their dress consisted of a cotton skirt (either blue or red and white striped), a low-necked blouse with short sleeves, a kerchief tied like a turban covering their hair, and bracelets, necklaces, and earrings of blue glass beads. Martínez added that the naturalists were approached by a number of women who "demonstrated by their actions the poverty and lack of morality of the inhabitants of this island."[7]

A graphic account of life in the Cape Verdes is Espada's description of a native shack. It was built of black basaltic stones and had a black roof made of dried leaves of banana trees. The inhabitants were very black Negroes, completely nude. They had a dirty black dog with shaggy fur, and in front of the hut some pieces of blackened meat were drying in the sun. "What desolate misery," he wrote, "and if it is painful to think of the extremes to which man has risen or degenerated, then the idea of what could be wished for or loved in this perpetual 'no man's land' is a horrible extreme."[8]

Scientific items collected on São Vicente included volcanic and sandstone rocks, 2 lizards, 2 birds, several spiders and insects, 221 plants belonging to 21 species, and numerous mollusks and zoophytes, the latter including unusual examples of coral. Some of the examples were collected during an excursion five miles inland to Lameyron Spring, the only source of fresh water on that island. Along the way the humidity and heat were so intense that the Spaniards were perspiring all over. At the spring they unloaded their knapsacks and had a typically Mediterranean lunch of bread, ham, cheese, sardines, olives, raisins, and wine.[9]

---

[7] Martínez, "*Diario,*" Aug. 22, 1862, AMCN; Jiménez de la Espada, *Diario,* 10–11, 21; Barreiro, *Historia,* 60; Almagro, *Breve,* 10.

[8] Jiménez de la Espada, *Diario,* 24.    [9] *Ibid.,* 10–11, 23–24.

Upon their return to port they found the ship's officers hostile. Trouble between the scientists and officers of the *Triunfo* began in the Canary Islands, developed into a full-blown dispute in the Cape Verdes, and continued until the two groups finally separated in Chile. A series of complaints about the odors resulting from dissecting and preserving specimens led to the complete barring of such activity aboard the ship, the officers asserting that navy regulations prohibited it. As a result, many of the items collected were thrown overboard. Martínez then discovered that the *Triunfo* officers would not permit him to get his special tin boxes from the storeroom, and his fish specimens were lost by putrefaction. In addition to a few metal boxes, the naturalists had brought aboard a supply of tin plate, which Paz, president of the commission and a former navy captain, assured them would be made into containers by the ship's armorer. But the latter refused to co-operate, even though they promised to pay him.[10]

Another point of conflict concerned the use of small boats belonging to the frigate. From time to time the scientists asked for a boat for transportation and to get fish and mollusk specimens, but their requests were usually refused. In view of this opposition they determined to go ashore at every opportunity and secure hotel rooms where they could carry out their activities, even though it would mean spending almost all of their small salary.

Commenting on the civil-military clash, Amor noted that their treatment was in complete contradiction to what they had been promised in Madrid, while Martínez said that Captain Croquer "was very angry at everything we were doing on a warship . . . he was a tyrant with the bearing of a sergeant, badly educated and foul mouthed." Some weeks later in a letter to one of the professors at the University of Madrid, he wrote that "aboard a warship there are many obstacles making it impossible to carry out a commission like ours."[11] It is interesting to observe that on previous Spanish scientific

[10] Martínez, *"Diario,"* Aug. 22–23, 1862, AMCN.

[11] Amor's remarks in Barreiro, *Historia*, p. 64. Martínez, *"Diario,"* Aug. 23, 1862, AMCN; Martínez to Laureano Pérez Arcas, Desterro, 18 Nov., 1862, Barreiro, *Historia*, p. 442.

expeditions the scholars and naval officers had co-operated closely. Perhaps that was due to better planning and careful personnel selection.

Before leaving the Cape Verde Islands, Almagro and Martínez had dinner aboard the flagship with the commander of the expedition, Admiral Pinzón. The conversation soon dealt with the dispute aboard the *Triunfo*, Pinzón affirming that the troubles were not caused by the navy but by the president of the scientific commission, Paz y Membiela, "who opposed everything and complained constantly." The Admiral told them that he had wanted the naturalists aboard the *Resolución*, but Paz had objected, saying there would be more room on the other ship.[12] Later that evening Martínez wrote in his diary that the Admiral's statements "confirmed my suspicions about the egoism of the person who is supposed to direct us, whose decisions are never correct," adding that some things said would be left in silence since he would never forget them.[13] The naturalists were impressed with Captain de la Rígada of the flagship, and they admired the high principles and friendship of Pinzón. They asked the Admiral "in the name of science" to do something to remedy the situation, but it seems there was little Pinzón could do.

During the next two weeks the frigates were under way for Bahia, Brazil, the flagship going by way of Pernambuco. Aboard the *Triunfo*, Captain Croquer obliged the scientists to comply with fine points of navy regulations, even forbidding them to go on deck—they had to remain in their quarters except for meals. Furthermore, he stationed a guard with fixed bayonet in the passageway to assure compliance with his order. An exception was made on August 27 when there was gunnery practice, and the civilians discovered their role in case of combat was to carry shells from the magazine to the gun battery. Their monotony was relieved two days later when a flying fish suddenly came through a porthole, landing in the stateroom. Martínez and Espada studied the fish and secretly preserved it, adding it to their collection.[14]

[12] *Ibid.*, 165.   [13] Martínez, *"Diario,"* Aug. 24, 1862, AMCN.
[14] *Ibid.*, Aug. 27–29, 1862, AMCN.

When the naturalists approached the mainland of America, they were overwhelmed by the sight. "What a spectacle after sixteen days of sailing between sky and sea," Espada said in his diary. The land looked, he went on to say, like a green oasis covered with coconut palm trees that grew out of the water. The earth in the few spots where they could observe it was as red as a copper mine; and the sweet aromas of the fertile land came out to sea, intoxicating them, while a multitude of web-footed birds escorted the ship to its anchoring place.[15]

[15] Jiménez de la Espada, *Diario*, 12, 28.

# IV

# The Empire of Brazil

The Spanish scientists aboard the *Triunfo* entered the Brazilian port of Bahia on September 9, 1862. Before anchoring, the frigates hoisted Brazilian flags to the top of their main masts and saluted the city, their salvos being returned by the fortress guarding the bay. In the city the naturalists secured rooms at the Hotel Fertin, where they lived while working on their collections during the following three weeks. Having promised an offering to the Holy Virgin if they arrived safely in America, they gave their thanks in a monastery dedicated to Our Lady of Sorrows.[1]

Capital of Brazil from 1549 to 1763, the city was founded as São Salvador da Bahia de Todos os Santos, subsequently shortened to Bahia and now called Salvador. Almagro noted that Bahia's population was over 100,000, the majority being Negroes, some free and some slave. Sugar, coffee, tobacco, rare woods such as the dyewood called brazilwood (*Caesalpinia echinata*), and diamonds were the principal exports. He said the old capital was a progressive city, boasting "most of the innovations of the century."[2]

Entries in the diaries of the Spanish naturalists show their enthusiasm about the panoramic scenery of Bahia. They tell of hills plunging sharply into the bay, tall palm trees and luxurious vegetation surrounding the white houses and hiding some of them like nests in foliage, and whales gathered in the magnificent bay, where they were "fished" within sight of the inhabitants. The city was built on two levels, one along the narrow strip adjacent to the water, the other much higher, on top of the hills overlooking the bay.

[1] Almagro, *Breve*, 11–12.
[2] *Ibid.*

*30*

Zigzag roads and a primitive funicular connected the two areas. The lower city, older and dirtier, had warehouses, offices, and shacks for the poor, while the upper ridge supported the cathedral and houses of the well-to-do. In 1830 the lower city had been enlarged by the building of a new street over the water, the buildings and roadway being supported on pilings.[3]

The second day in port, the naval officers and naturalists paid official calls on local authorities. Accompanied by the Spanish vice-consul, they crossed the lower city on foot, then were taken to the upper zone in twenty-four sedan chairs, each one carried by two robust Negroes. Astonished and repelled by this mode of transport, the Spaniards were at first hesitant to use it, but they finally acceded. Almagro said the palanquins were painted bright blue, ornately decorated and gilded, surmounted by a cupola in the form of a crown from which tapestries were hung. When the procession reached the upper level of Bahia, they used six horse-drawn carriages to visit the houses of the provincial governor, archbishop, commanding general, chief of police, and head of the arsenal. In the next few days friendly authorities and residents of the city organized several dinners and two balls in honor of the Iberian guests.[4]

The weeks in Bahia were crowded with trips to near-by points. On a three-day trip to Itaparica Island, some twelve miles off the coast, the naturalists augmented their collections of flora and fauna. The island, about thirty-five miles long, had tropical vegetation growing in soils formed from decomposed granite and sandstone. There were also large deposits of clay, from which the islanders made a variety of pottery vases and dishes. Landing at a sandy beach, the Spaniards and their Brazilian companions set up camp near the principal town of Porto de Todos os Santos. Their campground was littered with whale bones because there was a plant near by for the extraction of oil from the sea mammals. On the island they collected specimens ranging from plants to insects, lizards, worms, shellfish, echinoderms,

---

[3] Jiménez de la Espada, *Diario*, 27–29; Martínez, *"Diario,"* Sept. 9, 1862, AMCN.
[4] Almagro, *Breve*, 12.

fish, and birds. The rarest items were a toad and a frog with horizontal elliptical eye pupils. Espada said they shot the lizards, since "in this country lizards do not run, they fly, and once they enter the brush no one can catch them." Shotguns were also used to bring down birds of such wide variety that "with each shot we killed a different species."[5] The Spaniards, amazed that the birds did not fly away with the noise of the gun blast, found shooting them easy but locating the downed birds in the thick grass and brush so difficult that they lost more than half of them. Espada was excited when, with his bare hands, he caught a hummingbird that was resting on the ground. It was the first time he had seen one of these delicate creatures alive. Although most of the naturalists wanted to stay longer, they were obliged to return to the mainland when the president of the commission could find no unusual examples of seashells for his personal collection.[6]

A few days later the naturalists went by railroad into the primitive forest of Brazil. Leaving Bahia at eight in the morning, they rode to Pitagua, the end of the line, where they arrived about noon. Between patches of jungle and forest they saw cleared fields and small plantations of sugar cane, cotton, and maize, but "few places where the hand of civilized man had made itself felt." The forest was so thick at Pitagua that they could not penetrate it, even to collect specimens. Observing tropical termites at one of the station stops, Amor quickly gathered nine species, some of which infested the area so thickly that they caused incalculable damage. Their nests in the trees were shaped like eggs and often measured three feet in diameter. Inside were cells where phalanges of the insects lived. The insects had constructed vaulted passageways along the tree trunks from their nests to the ground, so that they were able to move a long distance completely hidden from view. Because insects in Brazil attacked ripe, dry tobacco, it was cut green and smoked humid.[7]

[5] Marcos Jiménez de la Espada to Mariano Paz Graells, Rio de Janeiro, Nov. 3, 1862, Jiménez de la Espada, *Diario*, 13–15; see also 31–32.

[6] *Ibid.*, 13–14.

[7] *Ibid.*, 37; Martínez, *"Diario,"* Sept. 26, 1862, AMCN.

On another occasion the Spaniards visited near-by Lake Dile, accompanied by four men from Bahia interested in natural science. Leaving the city at five in the morning, they reconnoitered the area in a large canoe paddled by a Negro guide. "The majestic silence of the lake was only disturbed by songs of the birds or the flight of bats frightened by the movement of the trees," wrote Martínez, who also noted that there were other boats on the lake, piloted by Negroes dressed in black trousers, black jackets, and black straw hats.[8] The object of the trip was to measure the water temperature at various depths and to collect biological specimens. Plant life was abundant, as were fish and birds, especially partridges and ducks. Orchids were hanging from tree branches and even growing out of birds' nests. The naturalists returned with a variety of things, including snakes, turtledoves, and mollusks. One item left behind was a bug removed from Martínez' finger, where it had inserted itself.[9]

Between trips to the surrounding countryside the scientists visited some of the public buildings of Bahia. On a visit to the hospital and school of medicine they saw a very fine collection of animal skeletons prepared by the students. The city's public library, Martínez noted, contained 16,000 volumes, but there was not a book in Spanish or any American Indian language, nor was there a catalog or index to the holdings. In the reading room an inscription said that the library had been founded in 1811 by the governor and captain general, Conde dos Arcos. The Lyceum, located in a former convent, had a fine display of costumes and arms used by Indians of Pará, Brazil; and the natural history section had many examples of plants, mammals, and birds, "all badly prepared and cared for." Nevertheless, the Spaniards made several trips there, mainly to get the local names for some of their specimens.[10]

Visiting a factory where lime was extracted from seashells and coral, the naturalists got some samples to send home. They fre-

[8] *Ibid.*, Sept. 24, 1862, AMCN.
[9] *Ibid.*; Jiménez de la Espada, *Diario*, 38.
[10] Martínez, "*Diario*," Sept. 29, 1862, AMCN.

quented local markets looking for novel types of vegetables, fruits, fish, and fowl. Meanwhile, as often as they could arrange it, they had a detachment of sailors from the *Triunfo* fish and drag the bay for unusual marine specimens.

Antonio de Lacerda, a well-to-do businessman, was one of several local residents interested in natural science who gave the visitors items for their collections and accompanied them on excursions to near-by points. His country house on the edge of Bahia was surrounded by a veritable botanical and zoological garden, and the villa itself was like a museum, with collections of Brazilian biological specimens and minerals, including diamonds. His excellent library and well-equipped laboratory had a number of attractions, including the finest microscope that Martínez had ever seen. With his wife's help Lacerda operated a small meteorological observatory, sending data to European stations. The Spaniards, dinner guests on several occasions, were presented with samples of seeds, plants, woods, birds' nests, and minerals. One Sunday afternoon the visitors invited Lacerda to join them in the botanical garden, where the Spanish squadron band presented a concert, but there was little else they could do to repay his abundant hospitality and generosity.[11]

Lacerdo made arrangements for Almagro, the anthropologist-physician, to examine a Brazilian Indian. The indigenous Tupinambas had disappeared completely from the region around Bahia, but there was a nine-year-old Patashó Indian girl living in the city. Called Dionisia by her foster parents, she had been recently found among a group of dead Indians after a battle between her tribe and a neighboring one. The girl ate raw meat, uttered only "inarticulate savage cries," and had been branded on her abdomen with the sign of her tribe. When Almagro first tried to measure her to construct an anthropometric chart, she broke into tears, but he soon had her smiling by using the instruments on himself first. Some notes taken at the time by Espada indicate that she had long coarse hair of a dull black color, her dark eyes were slanted and widely spaced, she was snub-nosed and had a short mouth and convex upper lip, and her face in

[11] *Ibid.*, Sept. 21, 1862, AMCN.

*34*

Members of the Scientific Commission of the Pacific, before leaving
Madrid, 1862. Left to right, front: Bartolomé Puig, Fernando Amor,
Patricio Paz, Francisco Martínez, Rafael Castro; rear: Juan Isern,
Marcos Jim'enez de la Espada, Manuel Almagro.

The Spanish frigate *Triunfo*, 1862.

Aboard the *Triunfo*, 1862.

The waterfront, Bahia, Brazil, September, 1862.

A view of the city of Rio de Janeiro and Sugar Loaf Mountain,
October, 1862.

The Imperial Library at Rio de Janeiro, October, 1862.

The Museum of Natural Sciences, Rio de Janeiro, October, 1862.

The Santa Teresa section of Rio de Janeiro, October, 1862.

The Plaza of Desterro, Santa Catarina Island, Brazil, November, 1862.

The Hotel Vapor in Desterro, Santa Catarina Island, November, 1862.

Four members of the expedition with an Indian boy, Montevideo,
Uruguay, December, 1862. The Spaniards are, left to right: Manuel
Almagro, Juan Isern, Marcos Jiménez de la Espada, Francisco Martínez.

A view of Valparaíso, Chile, May, 1863.

The harbor (Plazuela de la Bolsa) at Valparaíso, May, 1863.

Volunteer firefighters at Valparaíso, May, 1863.

Hotel de l'Union at Valparaíso, May, 1863.

The Spanish schooner *Covadonga*.

general was well developed. A portrait of this girl taken by Castro shows clearly her sad and pensive expression.[12]

Espada, visiting an ostrich farm near Bahia, proposed buying some of the live birds for the Madrid Zoological Garden; but this proposal led to an argument with the president of the commission. Paz objected on the grounds that the group was authorized only to collect items for the Museum of Natural Science in the Spanish capital. Espada later recalled that during the argument he told Paz "to go to a place whose name I do not care to remember." A junta of the scientists settled the dispute by agreeing to meet in the future to vote on such purchases, and they authorized Espada to buy the ostriches. But by this time it was too late—the birds had been sold to someone else in the meantime. The next day they were able to purchase some live animals, including a puma and five monkeys.[13]

Contention among the Spanish scientists worsened during negotiations regarding the purchase of some bird collections. Frederic Chuchú, a French resident of Bahia, had two rather complete collections of birds of that area which he offered for sale at a moderate price; but Espada, who wanted to buy at least one of them for the museum, was waiting until the last moment in the hope of getting a better figure. Meanwhile, Puig bought one of the groups for his personal collection, forcing the price up for the remaining one. Espada remarked that Puig's conduct on this occasion was not the best, but he noted that the precedent had been set by Paz, who often bought outstanding examples for his own use.[14]

The finest collection the scientists obtained in Bahia was a group of reptiles given Espada by a German physician named Otto Vucherer. Along with a representative selection from his menagerie, the donor furnished data on their nomenclature, habitat, and diet. Established in Brazil for some years, Vucherer maintained relations with museums in Europe and Great Britain, sending them live and preserved speci-

---

[12] Jiménez de la Espada, *Diario*, 33; Almagro, *Breve*, 13, says Dionisia belonged to Tapajos tribe.
[13] Jiménez de la Espada, *Diario*, 14–16.
[14] *Ibid.*, 15.

mens. Espada's diary records interesting and curious phenomena observed by the German as well as legends about Brazilian animals. One story was about the "Catholic bird" (*Galbula viridis*), so named because it supposedly never worked on Sundays.[15]

After three days of farewell calls and dinners the Spanish scientists boarded the *Triunfo* again and sailed from Bahia the first of October, 1862. The six-day voyage to Rio de Janeiro was like the first part of their trip; diary entries record seasickness and continued feuding between naval officers and civilian passengers. Ashore, the passengers had found liberty and friendliness, but aboard ship they encountered hostility and virtual captivity. Again the scientists were temporarily prohibited from sitting on deck, a guard with saber in hand enforcing the order. Captain Croquer, shielding his action behind a fine point of naval regulations, was criticized by Martínez in his diary for depriving them of even small comforts. Another aspect of the dispute was related to the officers' mess. The scientists were informed that they could no longer dine with the ship's officers and that they would have to pay for all meals, even while lodged in a hotel while in port. The captain was able to enforce this order because the group received their pay and allowances through the squadron disbursing officer.[16]

Although members of the commission were supposed to have a detail of sailors at their service, this too was denied. On October 4 all crewmen were specifically forbidden to give assistance to the scientists, the captain threatening to "shoot anyone aiding them." He made this threat when he found the door to the photographer's cabin lying in the passageway—the wind and movement of the ship had blown it open with such a jolt that it fell to the floor. Another time the captain forbade anyone to catch the strange birds that appeared on the ship's railings, but he did not stop the naturalists from netting butterflies that occasionally swarmed over the ship.[17]

When the *Triunfo* approached Rio de Janeiro early in the morning

[15] *Ibid.*, 39.
[16] *Ibid.*, 40–41; Martínez, *"Diario,"* Oct. 1, 2, 4, 1862, AMCN.
[17] Jiménez de la Espada, *Diario*, 40–43; Martínez, *"Diario,"* Oct. 4, 1862, AMCN.

of October 6, the Spaniards were astonished by the spectacular panorama. The bay in front of them was dotted with a few green islands and a multitude of white sails. Rising out of the bay were hills with capricious forms, and a higher cordillera of jagged mountains formed a backdrop to the scene. The city's buildings stood out just beyond a white line marking the adjacent sandy beach. One of the ship's officers pointed out forts, islands, and the peaks called Pão de Açúcar (Sugarloaf), Corcovado (Hunchback), and El Gigante (The Giant). "The spectacle of the bay is grandiose, indescribable," remarked Espada.[18]

After exchanging the customary gun salute with Fort Villegaignon, the frigates anchored in the deep water of Guanabara Bay. Besides many Brazilian merchant ships and warships, two vessels from Great Britain and three from France were at anchor. The Spanish ships were superior to all the rest in their construction and appearance, according to Espada, who said, "We appeared among them like two swans in a flock of ducks."[19]

Searching for a suitable hotel in Rio de Janeiro with living and working space for eight people proved to be an interesting but impossible task. Espada said that with a few exceptions most of the hotels were full of "disreputable women who sell what they ought to cherish," and he warned the innocent traveler to "close his eyes, ears, and the door of his room," but even then he would have to put up with shouting and dancing of the nightly bacchanalia.[20] It was not possible to find accommodations for all the scientists in one hotel, so they split up. Paz, Martínez, Puig, Isern, and Castro stayed in the Hotel Luiz, the first two occupying rooms just vacated by some prostitutes. The other three members were near by at the Hotel des Frèyres Provençaux, where they had clean and comfortable rooms, excellent service, and tasty meals. Dominating the lobby was a large mural depicting gross debaucheries during a festival of Dionysus, with a motto in Latin advising, "Either drink or get out." The moral license of this tropical city shocked the provincial Spaniards.[21]

[18] Jiménez de la Espada, *Diario*, 42, 48–49.  [19] *Ibid.*, 50.
[20] *Ibid.*, 42, 51.  [21] *Ibid.*, 42, 52–53.

Once settled in Rio, the commission members met to take care of unfinished business and make plans, Martínez, as secretary, keeping notes of deliberations, disputes, and decisions. In addition to letters to Madrid, they drafted a letter to Admiral Pinzón asking to remain in port about two months. For orientation and assistance in Brazil they called on Spanish diplomatic and consular officials to find out how to get in touch with local scientists.[22]

While the Spanish consul in Rio received them in a formal, businesslike way, the ambassador to Brazil, Juan Blanco del Valle, was friendly, enthusiastic, and helpful. Receiving the commissioners in his hotel suite on the edge of the city, he offered them cigars and refreshments and promised to present them to Emperor Dom Pedro II of Brazil, who was seriously interested in science. He told them about court life at Petrópolis, the summer capital, where the royal family and high government officials lived. Petrópolis, he said, was a delightful retreat situated in a valley about two-thirds of a mile above sea level but only forty miles north of Rio and connected with it by railroad. He also talked about the Emperor, noting that he had "restricted powers and a small salary of $400,000, little patrimony, and could not maintain a court of magnates holding lucrative and honorific posts."[23] He explained that the people of Brazil ruled through their representatives, who supported humanitarian and utilitarian institutions, rejecting those considered showy or superfluous. This was quite a contrast to the flamboyant Queen of Spain and her ostentatious palaces and ceremonies.

The Spanish naturalists had two audiences with the Brazilian monarch, the first on October 20, 1862. Martínez' diary records some details of the meeting and his impressions during the two-hour conference. He said the palace was modest, not sumptuous, and built on a site overlooking beautiful views. The Emperor, dressed in a plain black coat and wearing a Spanish decoration, the Cross of Charles III, received them in a room bedecked with Spanish flags and coats of arms. Speaking in Spanish, he inquired about the goals of the expedi-

[22] *Ibid.*, 43.
[23] *Ibid.*, 44, 55.

tion and the special interest of each member. During the interview he demonstrated his familiarity with scientific terms and the names of well-known European scientists. Later he talked about the flora of Brazil and offered them unlimited use of the royal hunting lodge, Santa Cruz, about fifty miles southwest of Rio, where they could augment their collections. Espada and an assistant spent several days there gathering a multitude of items.[24]

A month in Rio de Janeiro gave the Spaniards time to explore the city and visit its suburbs. With a population of about 800,000 the capital had narrow, dirty streets downtown but wider ones in the outskirts. Martínez said the city "resembled a spider with its legs spread out between the hills." The outlying parts of Rio fascinated Espada, who noted that the many white houses had a myriad of windows and balconies, walls covered with crimson poinciana or purple bougainvillea, and gardens ablaze with colorful begonias. He observed that healthy breezes and a profusion of royal palms and banana trees made these areas shady, attractive, and pleasant. At night the gardens were lighted with many candles, the romantic settings enhanced by the perfume of jasmine and rhododendron.[25]

Notable public buildings and monuments of Brazil's capital were the charity hospital, central military barracks, aqueduct, hospital for the insane, imperial library, and natural history museum. The men saw several large plazas with fountains, one of which—Rocio Plaza—was dominated by an equestrian statue of the first emperor of Brazil. The four sides of the pedestal of this bronze monument symbolized the four great rivers of Brazil: Amazon, Pará, São Francisco, and Rio Grande. Rio's churches were of a heavy baroque style, "not pleasing to the eye," and the old royal palace "an unpretentious house which a Spanish nobleman might disdain." The city's two theaters received the most severe disapprobation, the dramatic theater being characterized as "a building in bad taste, as ugly inside as out," while the lyric theater was judged "worse yet."[26]

[24] Martínez, *"Diario,"* Oct. 20, 1862, AMCN.
[25] *Ibid.*, Oct. 12, 1862, AMCN; Jiménez de la Espada, *Diario*, 55.
[26] *Ibid.*, 54.

A public park and the botanical garden in Rio offered attractive sites for family outings, as well as serving as laboratories for botany students. In the park, adjacent to the bay, were handsome statues, orchid-covered arbors, an outdoor restaurant, kiosks, some obelisks donated by the Emperor, and an artificial lake with a sight-seeing launch. Swans, ducks, and a manatee swam about in the lagoon. The botanical garden was located in an attractive valley on the edge of the city where natural waterfalls and cascades tumbled down from adjacent mountains. Between lakes and rivulets were mangrove thickets, bamboo groves, native American plants, areas for ornamental flowers and herbs, a greenhouse, and pergolas covered with bluebells, vanilla plants, and other climbers. Plants representing all the continents bore labels giving their scientific names and habitats.[27]

The economic life and the class structure visible in Rio de Janeiro interested the Spaniards. Most of the inhabitants seemed to be involved in buying, selling, and transporting merchandise. In this commercial class were 30,000 French and 100,000 Portuguese citizens, according to Almagro. The small shopkeepers, poor people, foreign workers, and slaves lived and worked in the center near the water front; aristocrats, wealthy residents, and foreign ambassadors had villas on the outskirts of the city. Espada thought the upper class had little influence on general society and customs, partly because the nobility was not hereditary and partly because of the special organization of the state.[28]

Calling Negro slavery "a memento of Brazil's recent barbaric past," Espada noted that the institution was disappearing, that slave trade was prohibited, and that slaves could "easily" acquire their own freedom. Except for Negroes who had certain needed professions or skills and those who had borne arms for Brazil, former slaves had to leave the empire as soon as they became free. As for miscegenation, he observed that it was rare to find a Brazilian without African blood in his veins, and "on seeing someone who is pure white you can be sure

[27] *Ibid.*; Martínez, *"Diario,"* Oct. 12, 1862, AMCN.
[28] Almagro, *Breve*, 15.

that he is not from Brazil."[29] (Slavery persisted in Brazil for another twenty-seven years, until it was eliminated in 1889.)

At the same time that free Negroes were expelled from Brazil, colonists from Europe, especially Germans, were encouraged and aided by the imperial government. These immigrants received land in the interior and southern provinces, where they were expected to introduce European culture little by little. The Indians of Brazil lived in the jungle and did not figure in the national life. They were portrayed by Espada as being less civilized and less tractable than those conquered by the Spaniards on the other side of the Andes Mountains. Almagro observed that the Indian element had completely disappeared from Rio de Janeiro and Bahia, the two largest cities of Brazil.[30]

In connection with their scientific studies Paz and Espada visited the museum of natural history, where they were received "coldly and indifferently" even after identifying themselves as visiting scholars. The institution was only a few years old, and the collections a result of donations, purchases, and the work of a scientific commission of professors headed by a German resident, Dr. Frey. This group no longer functioned on account of a shortage of funds. Espada rated the museum good in minerals, fair in birds and plants, medium in mammals, and very bad in reptiles, fish, fossils, and shells. The insect collection was a total loss because of poor preparation of the specimens. Both he and Martínez, who visited the museum a few days later, admired the extensive display of Indian costumes, utensils, and weapons. They were surprised to find a good assortment of antiquities from Egypt, Greece, Rome, and Western Europe.[31]

Auguste Bourget, a young Frenchman who lived in Rio and sold objects of natural history, was an enthusiastic guide and adviser to the Spanish naturalists. He even showed Martínez how to prepare skins and stuff animals, a useful skill since Puig, the Spanish taxidermist,

[29] Jiménez de la Espada, *Diario*, 56.
[30] *Ibid.*, 56–57; Almagro, *Breve*, 14.
[31] Jiménez de la Espada, *Diario*, 45; Martínez, *"Diario,"* Oct. 15, 1862, AMCN.

"did very little and that poorly and unwillingly." Bourget's specialty being hummingbirds, he offered to sell the Spaniards a spectacular collection of 160 species. The commission, meeting to decide on this and other purchases, agreed to buy the birds. The French commercial naturalist also introduced the visitors to other naturalists and collectors in Rio, including Martem, a bird fancier, and Santo, a rich banker who had a private zoological garden at his villa on the edge of the city. Martínez observed that Santo's zoo had an elephant, gorillas and monkeys, lions, leopards, ounces (*Felis uncia*), deer, gazelles, a jaguar, coati, hyena, tapir, and the rodents agouti and cavy. His menagerie included the following birds: vultures, ibis, ostriches, pheasants, cranes, and herons.[32]

The French naturalist, Bourget, organized the outing and served as guide when the Spaniards climbed the rugged mountain, Corcovado, which rises 2,300 feet above the city of Rio de Janeiro. Starting at two in the morning and outfitted with khaki field clothes and knapsacks, the little band followed a path along the aqueduct. Although they carried shotguns to bring down bird specimens, Espada was reluctant to fire his weapon, saying he preferred one bird on the wing to a hundred in the hand.[33]

Espada's diary contains an emotional but well-written description of the ascension and the view from the summit of Corcovado. The night was dark and the trail marked by watery ruts, which they occasionally stumbled into, but all the discomforts were minimized under the magic of a spring night in the tropics. The jungle growth on each side of the path was thick; palm and banana trees were interlaced with lianas and orchids. Water ran in torrents along the surface of the mountain, bouncing off granite rocks, and the resulting spray humidified the atmosphere. From time to time fireflies crossed in front of them like meteors, and when they looked back at the sleeping city, the pattern of lights looked like a huge constellation that had fallen from the sky. The flapping of birds' wings and their exotic cries filled the air, the constant tapping of woodpeckers furnishing a

[32] *Ibid.*, Oct. 9–12, 1862, AMCN.
[33] Jiménez de la Espada, *Diario*, 58, 60.

basic rhythm. Songs of nocturnal birds, croaking of toads, chewing sounds of unknown insects, murmur of running water, aromas from tropical plants, and rustling movements in the shadows "revealed that mysterious creation that flees from the sun ... in order to devote itself to its loves, robberies, wars, all of which offends our imagination in a strange way."[34]

Halfway up Corcovado the naturalists reached The Roundtable, a protected resting place for climbers. The second half was steeper; they had to grasp roots and branches and stop frequently to rest. Arriving at the summit just before sunrise, Espada gave a shout, "Long Live Spain!" and sat down to rest while contemplating the changing colors of sky, water, and land. The view from the top encompassed the city, the adjacent hills and mountains, the bay with its islands, and the vast ocean, whose limits seemed to touch the even vaster sky. Thinking particularly of the Negro slaves, Espada asked, "Would anyone viewing Rio de Janeiro from this mountain call it a valley of tears? Although there are those below who cry, from this altitude they cannot be seen or heard, and heaven is closer to us than to them."[35] He then reflected on the opulence of Brazil—its fishing and maritime potential, fertile soil supporting crops and forests, mineral deposits, and rivers and fresh water sources, while life itself flourished in this tropical kingdom.

Descending Corcovado in the morning hours proved easier than the ascent in the dark of night, and the naturalists had time to examine the ecology of the peak. Medicinal plants and species of trees were pointed out by another climber, J. Nadeaud, surgeon aboard the French frigate *Pandora*. Having spent two years in Brazil, he had climbed Corcovado several times and was a competent botanist, specializing in ferns. When the Spaniards returned to the city, their knapsacks were full of specimens: gneiss and marl, fossilized arthropods, toads and toadstools, wild herbs, flowers and fruits, luminous insects, beetles, and gaily plumed birds.[36]

[34] *Ibid.*, 58.
[35] *Ibid.*, 60–61.
[36] Martínez, *"Diario,"* Oct. 17, 1862, AMCN.

*43*

Another excursion was a three-day trip made by Paz and Martínez to Cabo Frio in search of common and unusual natural history items. They left Rio at daybreak on October 28 aboard the steamship *Ceres*, J. D. Rodríguez de Albuquerque Bloen, captain. The following day they went ashore at Macahé. Martínez commented, "We left at daybreak without breakfast, without a guide, without provisions, without any information, and finally with no plan, as always."[37] At Cabo Frio they collected some unusual mollusks before returning to the Brazilian capital.

In order to spend more time in Brazil the Spanish scientists stayed behind when the *Triunfo* and *Resolución* sailed for Uruguay on October 28, 1862. Admiral Pinzón agreed to send a ship for them in a month's time, the rendezvous to be in southern Brazil at Rio Grande do Sul. In Pinzón's correspondence with the Spanish Navy ministry he complained that he had not received definite instructions before or after leaving Spain regarding liaison of his operations with the plans of the scientific commission. The only exception occurred when, in response to one of his queries, he was ordered not to let the group of scientists detain his mission. Thus the naval officers set the pace for the combined expedition.

To make better use of their last month in Luso-America, members of the commission split into two companies: Espada, Isern, Puig, and Castro remained in the Rio area for another three weeks, while the other four went to Santa Catarina Island off the coast of Brazil. The first group gathered specimens in the outskirts of Rio, Petrópolis, and the royal retreat of Santa Cruz. Isern sent his collection of thousands of plants, well preserved and identified, to Madrid, where they have been available to botany students for a hundred years. Likewise, Espada sent boxes full of Braziliana to Spain: minerals, mammals, fish, birds, snakes, and amphibians. Some of the boxes were of tin for objects preserved in alcohol.[38]

Meanwhile, Paz, Amor, Martínez, and Almagro left for Santa

[37] *Ibid.*, Oct. 29, 1862, AMCN.
[38] Almagro, *Breve*, 14; Martínez, *"Diario,"* Nov. 1–6, 1862, AMCN.

Catarina Island on November 6 aboard the Brazilian steamship
*Tocantins*. The three-day passage was delightful. The water was
calm and the splendid treatment shown them by Captain Hipólito
Duarte and his brother, Cándido, was in sharp contrast to what they
had endured on the Spanish warship. Before docking at the insular
port of Desterro, the *Tocantins* passed through the mile-wide strait
separating the island from mainland Brazil. Passing close to the
island the naturalists observed that it was hilly and wooded and had
landscapes of great beauty.[39]

On their arrival at Desterro, chief city of the island and capital of
the province of Santa Catarina, the Spanish scientists found rooms at
the Hotel do Vapor, the only hostelry in town. Nossa Senhora do
Desterro, once known as Santa Catarina and renamed Florianópolis
in 1894, had about five thousand inhabitants in 1862. Grouped around
the central plaza were the town's most important buildings: the
principal church, city hall, post office, jail, mayor's residence, and
hotel. The Sisters of Charity administered a hospital on the edge of
town. Economic activity of the port had to do with the export of hides
and salted meat, but Desterro was also an important whaling station
and naval base.[40]

Residents of the island received the strangers hospitably, although
a number of boys followed them around commenting on their peculiar
dress and eyeing their equipment, especially Amor's butterfly net.
The cordiality and happiness of the people impressed Martínez, who
wrote that when they went to the modest house of a Negro laundress,
she invited them in, apologized for not having any cut flowers to offer
them, and inquired about the Queen of Spain. He described typical
shacks on the edge of town, as being covered with palm fronds and
furnished with a rustic table, wooden chests, and at times a bench or
stools. The diet of the people consisted of a small amount of manioc
flour, dried meat, and a little bacon, supplemented by fruit, milk, fish,
and game, when available. In addition to the profusion of beautiful

[39] Almagro, *Breve*, 15; Martínez, "*Diario*," Nov. 6–8, 1862, AMCN.
[40] Almagro, *Breve*, 15; Martínez, "*Diario*," Nov. 8–10, 1862, AMCN.

flowers growing all over the island, the natives made artificial bouquets from feathers, fish scales, and seashells.[41]

Island officials called on the visiting Spaniards, offering to give them introductions and help them during their stay. Invited to the theater one night, Martínez said that the performance was "notable only because in Desterro all the actors are men."[42] The Spanish consul, Carlos Duarte Silva, accompanied Martínez to the provincial Lyceum, where he introduced him to Professor Fritz Müller, a distinguished naturalist. In the latter's small house adjacent to the bay, Martínez examined some unusual examples of mollusks, annelids, and zoophytes. Professor Müller forwarded specimens to Germany, where he also published articles on his scientific discoveries. He and his children joined the Spanish naturalists when they combed the beach for shells and shellfish.[43]

In the middle of November the Spanish consul accompanied the visitors on a three-day trip to another part of the island. Riding orchid-garlanded horses, they passed alongside orange groves, sugar plantations, virgin forests, salty sloughs, and areas covered by large dunes—all within sight of the ocean and the imposing mountains of mainland Brazil. Stopping overnight at the fazenda of Antonio and Manuel Viel, they slept between luxuriously embroidered sheets and were served coffee and sugar grown on the Viel plantation. The owners complained of the poverty of their land, but Martínez said this was attributable to the ruinous agricultural practices common in all of Brazil. First men destroyed the forests, cutting the trees for firewood and charcoal. Then they burned the stumps and underbrush and, without further preparation, seeded plantations heavily with sugar, tobacco, pineapple, etcetera. Since they did not vary the crops or use fertilizers, the land was impoverished by the third harvest. Before leaving the fazenda, some boys demonstrated the local weapon used for hunting. Called a *bodoco*, it was a flexible bow that launched clay pellets. The party returned to Desterro by another route, equally picturesque and having a great variety of flora and fauna.[44]

41 *Ibid.*, Nov. 8–11, 1862, AMCN.    42 *Ibid.*, Nov. 9, 1862, AMCN.
43 *Ibid.*, Nov. 9–10, 1862, AMCN.    44 *Ibid.*, Nov. 15, 1862, AMCN.

Two other foreigners in Desterro took an interest in the work of the Spanish naturalists and aided them in their investigations. A. L. von Hoonholt, a German ship captain temporarily based there with a hydrographic commission, provided small boats for excursions to Isla de las Viñas, José Mendez Beach, and other points accessible by water. Martínez said Hoonholt could not have done more for them. The French consul, Dr. Schutel, entertaining the Spaniards socially, showed them some artifacts of Pará Indians, including two complete outfits of clothing, jewelry made of teeth, hammocks, and weapons. He had skeletons of a local Indian woman and her two children; these aborigines had been captured and brought to him alive but died soon thereafter of what he termed "sadness." Dr. Schutel gave a farewell party for the Iberian visitors when the rest of the commission arrived from Rio.[45]

Packing up to leave for Rio Grande do Sul, the Spaniards made notes about items caught, shot, fished, gathered, purchased, and received as gifts on Santa Catarina Island. Martínez entered in his diary the local names for twenty-nine kinds of fish he was sending to Spain; he also mentioned boxes of lichens, grasses, ferns, "the most beautiful orchids in the world," fruits such as one called *grumichama*, snakes, mollusks, luminous insects, butterflies, birds, and some strange frogs that produced a sound resembling a dog's bark. Another local species of the same order imitated perfectly the sound of beating drums.[46]

The passage from Santa Catarina to Rio Grande took four days in the small steamship *Emperatriz*. The packet was so crowded with passengers, mainly students returning home for vacation, that the Spanish scientists had to sleep on deck or wherever they could find space. Martínez, a quiet, meditative man, objected to the singing and incessant talking of the schoolboys. Reflecting on the situation of the commissioners aboard the *Emperatriz*—sleeping in chairs, the impossibility of doing any scientific work aboard, their problem of storing delicate instruments and excess baggage—he concluded that a

[45] *Ibid.*, Nov. 13, 25, 1862, AMCN.
[46] *Ibid.*, Nov. 21, 1862, AMCN.

scientific expedition needed its own means of transportation. He then berated his colleagues, saying, "Some members of the commission have done little more than enjoy themselves and buy things." A couple of days later and in the same mood he wrote, "I couldn't sleep, thinking of my country and my mistake in leaving it to endure so much unpleasantness."[47] On November 27 they reached the port of Rio Grande, and finding that the Spanish ship had not arrived, the naturalists had no alternative but to go ashore while waiting for their transportation.

Seven days they waited for the Spanish warship, expecting it each day, not daring to take any long excursions, and reluctant to unpack their scientific gear. Hotel accommodations were not good; Martínez said he had an inside room with no light, and he could not sleep well because of "bad odors, unpleasantness, and the continual noise of rodents running up and down the walls."[48] The terrain around Rio Grande was rather flat, monotonous, arid, and sandy. Close to the city there were sand dunes moved by the wind, often forming drifts along fence lines and against buildings. Some of the drifts were covered with turf and legumes. But the outstanding geographic feature in this area was a large salt-water lagoon called Lagoa dos Patos. Here the naturalists were able to collect unusual specimens of sea life, marsh plants, and aquatic birds.

Friendship with a distinguished local naturalist, Federico Albuquerque, made the Spaniards' delay in southern Brazil worth while. He showed them surprisingly good collections of fish, insects, parasitic plants, live birds, and mammals including a fox, all from southern Brazil and most of them from the province of Rio Grande do Sul. A number of his specimens were crated, ready to be shipped to another city where he planned to move; but ordering his servants to open the boxes, he gave the visitors assorted samples of his well-prepared specimens.[49]

Albuquerque furnished hunting gear, horses, and even a Negro

[47] *Ibid.*, Nov. 27, Dec. 1, 1862, AMCN.
[48] *Ibid.*, Nov. 27, 1862, AMCN.
[49] *Ibid.*

servant when he accompanied the Spaniards on several excursions. Martínez said the slave was a lively, intelligent, and helpful young man who took care of the hunting equipment and helped collect objects for which his congenial master offered rewards. On November 29 they fished with hand nets and screened the mud of shallow Lagoa dos Patos. While asking for drinking water at a house on an island in the lagoon, they witnessed a curious method of collecting and storing potable water; covered earthen jars were sunk into the ground and filled by gradual seepage. Visiting the area near the entrance to the lagoon, they met Captain Alvez dos Santos, who invited them to his home for dinner and showed them his large collection of shells from near-by beaches. It was raining hard the first of December, but Isern, Espada, Martínez, and others of the group mounted horses at five in the morning and hunted birds all day. In addition to identifying the birds, Albuquerque pointed out plant and animal species, including a large lizard which local people used for food, the scales serving as a fetish for curing chest illnesses. Another outing took them to a *fazenda* named Philantropis, where, in contrast to the barren topography near Rio Grande, the underbrush was so thick they had to use machetes to cut their way through it.[50]

Observing that the season was changing from spring to summer, with consequent biological change and development, Martínez became convinced that a proper survey of a region's flora and fauna must embrace collections at different seasons. Thus a scientific expedition, he said, must allow "time and repose for the observers to wait for development stages."[51] The diary of this Spanish naturalist contains scientific ideas and suggestive material not unlike the writings of Charles Darwin, Henry Bates, and Alfred Wallace, his English contemporaries who also observed nature in South America.

Finally on December 3 the Spanish schooner *Covadonga* anchored near Rio Grande, the captain ordering the scientists to embark the next day. They paid their bills, gathered together papers, personal effects, equipment, and curiosa, then took small boats out to the

[50] *Ibid.*, Nov. 29–Dec. 1, 1862, AMCN.
[51] *Ibid.*, Nov. 29, 1862, AMCN.

waiting vessel. Although the *Covadonga* was smaller and older than the *Triunfo*, the naturalists found it attractive compared to the dirty and disorganized frigate. Furthermore, during the three-day voyage to Montevideo they were treated well by the captain and officers, eating with them and enjoying the complete run of the ship, even the bridge. Martínez wrote in his diary that this reception made the severe discipline aboard the *Triunfo* seem even more ridiculous.[52]

As they were leaving Brazil, several of the Spanish naturalists jotted down impressions of their three months in that beautiful and exuberant country. One of them reflected that distinguished Brazilian men of science had been exceedingly friendly and generous, while everyone from poor fishermen to high officials had received them splendidly. Almagro was impressed by the potential for scientific study: virgin forests, colossal rivers, mountains, coastal plains—all with exotic plant and animal species waiting to be discovered and classified. Other members of the commission contrasted the Spanish Queen with the Emperor of Brazil, noting that the latter presented a good example to his subjects of public and private morality. In addition, his love of knowledge gave him stature in the eyes of the world.[53]

Four of the Spanish naturalists later returned to Brazil, descending the Amazon River from source to mouth, but when they left the empire in 1862, they all felt it might be forever.

[52] *Ibid.*, Dec. 4, 7, 1862, AMCN.
[53] Almagro, *Breve*, 17; Martínez, "*Diario*," Dec. 4, 1862, AMCN.

V

# Across the Pampas and Over the Andes

$A$RRIVAL of the *Covadonga* in Montevideo, Uruguay, on December 7, 1862, interested and excited the Iberian scientists, for this was their first visit to a Spanish-speaking part of Latin America. The first night ashore Martínez wrote in his diary, "The name Spanish America wakes so many memories in every Spaniard"; others recalled that the area was intimately connected to Spain by blood, culture, traditions, and three centuries of history.[1]

In the 1860's the Republic of Uruguay, situated between Brazil and Argentina, was noted for its great livestock ranches and exports of dried and salted meats. Almagro said the capital was "an agreeable city of about 40,000, all white, mostly of Spanish origin, but some Italians too."[2] The original Indians of that area, warlike Charruas, had disappeared, leaving but few traces in the blood and customs of the country. Although Uruguay had rich land resources, a favorable climate and geographical position, and ample markets for its agricultural exports—all of which should have brought prosperity and progress—the republic was in a lamentable state, brought about by political chaos and civil wars.

Spanish consular and diplomatic officials helped the visiting scientists considerably. The minister, Carlos Creus, entertained them in his home several times, introducing them to Uruguayan cultural and political figures. On December 11 he accompanied them on a visit to the home of the president of the republic, Bernardo Beno, who received them cordially, "talking about science and showing his collection of minerals." That same evening they gathered in the

[1] Martínez, *"Diario,"* Dec. 7, 1862, AMCN; Almagro, *Breve,* 17.
[2] *Ibid.*

garden of the Hotel Oriental for a concert by a group of musicians from the Spanish flagship. Two theaters provided entertainment on other evenings. The Solís Theater presented an opera composed in Buenos Aires titled *La Indígina,* but the other one offered "nothing worthwhile," according to Martínez.[3]

During their stay in Uruguay the Spaniards observed and collected native plants and animals. Martínez' diary records a visit to the "Museum of Natural History, if you could call it that," a small part of the public library where a few objects were poorly displayed. The director of the museum had no training or education in the sciences or skills in preparing specimens. A French resident of Montevideo, M. Tibert, had a notable collection of reptiles, skeletons, invertebrates, and plants, and the British chargé d'affaires, W. G. Etsom, was a dedicated amateur scientist who accompanied the Iberians on several forays, including a visit to a stone quarry in search of minerals.[4] The municipal market, in an old Spanish building with the colonial coat of arms still visible, was a good source for native products. Here Martínez acquired eggs of the American ostrich ñandú (*Rhea americana*), South American strawberries, Paraguayan tea called maté (*Ilex paraguayensis*), and seventeen kinds of fish. He failed in his attempt to get fishermen to bring him rare items even though specifically engaging them, "for as happens in this country, although they do not intend to do it, they promise they will."[5]

Excursions to seashore and countryside in search of items for their collections were frequent and rewarding. On a trip to the northwest of Montevideo the scenery reminded Martínez of central Spain—no trees and the land seeded to wheat and cereals. Ranch houses were constructed of mud supported by wooden poles and had thatched roofs, and adjacent livestock corrals were constructed with poles or old trees. Seeking drinking water, Paz, Amor, and Martínez entered a ranch foreman's house where they saw half a cow, pierced by an iron bar, being barbecued over a charcoal fire. Invited for lunch, the guests

---

[3] Martínez, "*Diario,*" Dec. 8, 18, 22, 1862, AMCN.

[4] *Ibid.,* Dec. 14, 17, 1862, AMCN.

[5] *Ibid.,* Dec. 13, 18, 27, 1862, AMCN.

ate typical cowboy fare, barbecued beef and milk. Later the Gauchos demonstrated their agility with lasso and bolas (stones tied together and thrown to entangle animals' legs), swiftly catching any animal pointed out. At another ranch the wandering scientists observed an *ombú* tree (*Phytolacca dioica*), famous in legend and history of the pampas. Fruit of this thick-trunked tree was used to kill rats, and chickens nested in its branches. On a hunting trip to the Solís River the Spaniards filled their bags with gold-necked doves, parrots, calendar larks, and gray plovers. The catch was "not glorious but abundant," said Espada.[6]

Inspection of the largest *saladero*, or meat-packing plant, in Uruguay proved interesting to the visiting Spaniards. An Englishman named Samuel Lafond owned the establishment, and it was managed by Enrique Hunzinger. Uruguay's wealth centered on extensive herds of cattle, horses, and sheep, whose hides, fats, wool, and meat were processed and exported. Dried and salted beef (jerky, *charquí*, or tasajo) was the most important product, most of which was sent to Brazil and Cuba, where it was fed to plantation slaves. Lafond's plant, about two hours out of Montevideo, had its own docks on the Plata River. During slaughtering season, November to March, about two hundred employees processed from eight to nine hundred head of cattle a day. Espada said the majority of the workers were Basques, who wore berets and worked hard in the dirty and smelly stockyards and buildings. Following a guided tour through the plant, the foreman served the visitors four plates of cooked meat cut from different parts of the same animal. "A curious lunch, but truthfully not very agreeable," said Espada.[7]

Back in Montevideo the naturalists met other people, some of whom had remarkable personal collections. Pedro Giral's assemblage was varied but not in good condition. A bird fancier, Jorge P. Livón, gave Espada and Martínez detailed information about American ostriches. He told them that the large birds put eggs around the edge

[6] *Ibid.*, Dec. 19, 21, 23, 1862, AMCN; Barreiro, *Historia*, 116.

[7] Espada's account dated Jan. 5, 1863, in *ibid.*, 508–11; Martínez, *"Diario,"* Jan. 5, 1863, AMCN.

of their nests, breaking them open to attract flies; then they feed their young on the flies. Livón agreed to forward some birds and eggs to Spain for the museums of that country. Vice-rector of Montevideo's university, Laurentino Jiménes, was interested in archaeology and history; he related anecdotes and gave the visitors artifacts and historical pamphlets. Another friend and informant was Juan Berner e Irigoyen, a native of Spain, who had traveled in many parts of South America, often accompanying noted scientists. In Montevideo, Berner served as president of a topographic commission. He was a distinguished calligrapher, having received medals from the governments of England, France, Spain, Brazil, Argentina, and Uruguay. He donated Indian arrowheads and articles of aboriginal clothing to the Spanish commission.[8]

When it came time to leave Montevideo, the discord between scientists and naval officers came to a climax. The principal antagonists were Enrique Croquer, captain of the *Triunfo*, and Patricio Paz, president of the commission; their enmity had begun before the squadron left Spain and grew as the trip progressed. In Montevideo, Paz broke completely with the captain, sending a long letter to Admiral Pinzón and to the Spanish Navy minister containing detailed complaints of poor treatment. Espada, who later saw a copy of the letter, remarked that it was "more notable for its correct language and penmanship than for its contents."[9]

President Paz, feeling that he could not continue aboard the warships, called a meeting of the scientific commission to resolve the dilemma. He presented two alternatives: return to Spain or continue overland to Chile and Peru. The junta decided on the latter course and proposed splitting the commission into two groups, one to go by land and the other by sea. Paz agreed, then named his closest friends to accompany him in the land force. Espada remarked it was strange that the seashell expert or conchologist should head the land team, and he protested when the botanist was ordered to go by sea, saying

[8] *Ibid.*, Dec. 27, 1862, AMCN.
[9] Espada to Mariano Paz Graells, Santiago, Chile, April 10, 1863, Jiménez de la Espada, *Diario*, 98–100.

Isern "could not collect plants on the high seas." It would have seemed natural that Espada, charged with collecting land reptiles, mammals, and birds, would also go overland, but he was sent by sea, because his relations with Paz were poor and because his associate, Puig the taxidermist, would not go by land. Finally the two groups were made up, more on the basis of friends and foes than on any logical scheme. Paz headed the land team, joined by Isern, Almagro, and Amor; the other four went with the naval squadron. They were to meet about four months later in Valparaíso, Chile, to compare notes and continue their labors.[10]

Other personality conflicts erupted in the heat of Uruguay's summer at the end of 1862. Paz censured the conduct of two commissioners, reporting to Madrid that Amor and Almagro "do nothing more than dance." Espada, covertly reading Paz's correspondence, characterized him with some choice unprintable terms and said, "I will never trust him, especially on my return to Madrid." Meanwhile, Martínez criticized some of his colleagues, complaining that they were only on the expedition to enjoy themselves. His diary reflects disapprobation of Admiral Pinzón with entries such as, "He was, as usual, enjoying life in union with persons of both sexes and bad reputations." Invited aboard the flagship on Christmas Day, Martínez was able to default when a sudden storm arose, freeing him from "the ominous dinner, especially since Pinzón was drunk." The next week when the captain of the *Triunfo* asked Martínez to dine with him, the latter commented that the evening was arranged "without doubt to relate gossip about Paz."[11] Bickering was reduced by at least 50 per cent when the two groups of naturalists went their separate ways.

The overland team left Montevideo on December 26, 1862. Traveling by stagecoach and steamship, they saw much of northwestern Uruguay before crossing into Argentina. On the three-day trip from Montevideo to Mercedes they crossed extensive grassy

[10] *Ibid.*

[11] Martínez, *"Diario,"* Dec. 25, 31, 1862, Jan. 2, 1863, AMCN; Jiménez de la Espada, *Diario,* 64.

plains that provided abundant pasturage for large herds of livestock. Almagro undoubtedly exaggerated when he wrote of "one ranch of twenty-five to thirty square miles with 10,000 to 12,000 head of cattle attended to by only one or two men." But there were ranches that large, and during much of the year livestock grazed freely on the range with no cowboys or fences in sight. The Spaniards were surprised and pleased when they saw large flocks of ostriches in the fields along the way. Near Mercedes, "a pretty town of about five thousand people," the naturalists boarded a steamer for a trip up the Uruguay River to Paysandú and Salto. After a few days in northern Uruguay they headed for Argentina, an easy transition achieved by crossing the river which serves as boundary. Almagro noted that the Uruguay River was dotted with a number of small islands and that its low banks were covered with shrubbery which concealed jaguars, enemy to man and cattle on that frontier. Descending the river to its mouth where it joins the Paraná River to form the Río de la Plata estuary, the overland group arrived at the capital of Argentina, Buenos Aires, on January 14, 1863.[12]

Meanwhile, Espada and Castro spent a few days in Buenos Aires, crossing the Río de la Plata on the steam ferry *Constitución*. The Spanish consul in the Argentine capital introduced the visitors to other compatriots living there and gave the naturalists information about important historical sites and monuments of the region. Espada's diary recalls visits to the cathedral, the Colón Theater, the Franciscan monastery, the plaza where Argentine independence was proclaimed, and a palace of former dictator Juan Manuel de Rosas. The national museum, directed by German zoologist C. G. Burmeister, was "very poor in mammals, birds, reptiles, and fish," but had a splendid collection of fossils, some of which were donated to Espada for Madrid's Museum of Natural Science.[13]

President Bartolomé Mitre of Argentina officially greeted the visiting Spaniards and unofficially met with them in January, 1863. In the first part of that month Admiral Pinzón crossed the estuary

[12] Almagro, *Breve*, 19–21.
[13] Jiménez de la Espada, *Diario*, 62–63.

from Montevideo on a good-will mission, arranged preliminaries of a treaty between Argentina and Spain, and signed an agreement concerning the nationality of Spaniards born in Argentina. President Mitre honored the Spanish squadron commander with a state banquet and later entertained the visiting scientists in his mansion. Almagro recalled that they met there a group of young Patagonian and Chaco Indians brought to the capital by the President for their education; he would "send them later to their regions to contribute to the civilization of those nations." Almagro thought the Platine republic had "much to gain from the good example and acknowledged patriotism of President Mitre."[14]

While Admiral Pinzón was in Buenos Aires, he had dealings with two other nations that were former colonies of Spain: Peru and Paraguay. The former's diplomatic representative in Argentina questioned at length the purpose of the Spanish visit to America and asked what attitude the fleet would show when they arrived in Peru. Pinzón replied that Spain was not hostile to Peru but would be firm regarding existing grievances. Meanwhile, he sent an agent to the Republic of Paraguay to study that country's attitude toward its former mother country. The officer's mission was successful; in addition to strengthening diplomatic ties he returned to Buenos Aires with some Paraguayan hardwood needed to repair the mast of the Spanish flagship.[15]

The overland group of Spanish naturalists remained in the Argentine capital for about two weeks, even though Isern complained that "the region doesn't offer much to a botanist." Almagro labeled Buenos Aires "the most important Spanish city in South America," noting that its population was about 150,000 and that it had handsome buildings and monuments, interesting museums, several theaters, and beautiful boulevards. His general comments about the republic are similar to his analysis of Uruguay; here again was a country blessed with favorable climate and fertile soil, but its develop-

---

[14] Almagro, *Breve*, 22–23; Jiménez de la Espada, *Diario*, 63; Esteban-Infantes, *Expediciones*, 257.

[15] *Ibid.*, 257–58.

ment was hindered by intermittent civil wars. Although there were a number of copper, lead, and gold mines, Argentina's principal source of wealth was agriculture. The vast area embracing the Pampas produced spontaneously a magnificent pasturage, feeding millions of head of livestock. Cotton and yerba maté were important crops in Entre Ríos and Corrientes provinces; sugar cane and coffee were harvested in Tucumán and Salta; and fruit orchards, grapes, and temperate-climate products flourished in San Juan and La Rioja.[16]

From Buenos Aires, Paz and company took a three-day boat ride up the Paraná River to Rosario, the jumping-off place for an overland journey to Chile. When they arrived on February 4, 1863, the Spanish consul in Rosario, forewarned of the visit, arranged a banquet and reunion of the Spanish colony at the largest hotel. A local military band provided music for the affair and for a similar function the following night at the home of a rich Spanish resident of the river port. Almagro recorded the population of Rosario as six thousand, noting that it had been double that size a few years earlier. Its short-lived boom coincided with the period when Buenos Aires Province was independent from the Argentine confederation; at that time provincial trade funneled through Rosario.[17]

Heading almost due west along the thirty-third parallel of south latitude, the Spanish scientists crossed the wide flatland of Argentina. They boarded a stagecoach in Rosario on February 10, destined for Córdoba, about 250 miles across pure pampas with no highway and not even a small town along the route. Pulled by twelve beautiful horses, each with its Gaucho rider, the diligence moved rapidly between stage stops. A special mounted guard of eight soldiers and a lieutenant, provided by the governor of Santa Fe Province, escorted the visitors on their trip west. Isern wrote to a friend, "The public, ignorant of the purpose of the escort, believed that condemned prisoners were in the carriage."[18]

[16] Almagro, *Breve*, 21–22; Isern to Felix Borrell y Font, Lima, Peru, Aug. 28, 1863, in *El Pabellón Médico*, Madrid, III, No. 113 (Oct. 14, 1863), pp. 451–52, hereafter cited as Isern letter II.

[17] Almagro, *Breve*, 23.

[18] Isern letter II.

Posts or stage stops were located about fifteen miles apart. At each one there was a hut and a corral. In the former lived the "master of the post," while the latter contained forty or fifty fine horses. When a coach arrived at the post, each rider unsaddled his horse and exchanged it for one in the corral, which he harnessed up. Then the coach started off again at a gallop. The stagecoach did not stop for lunch—passengers ate and drank what they brought along. Each night they camped at a post, where the Gauchos built a fire, killed a sheep, and either broiled or boiled the meat. Besides mutton they prepared their beloved drink of Paraguayan tea leaves—dried and pulverized—by putting them into a gourd and adding boiling water and sugar. Gauchos always drank this through a straw or thin tube called a *bombilla*. The horsemen slept in open air, and so did the Spanish naturalists after the first night, when they were besieged by bugs in the post shack. Almagro had a high opinion of Gauchos, saying they were lighthearted, accommodating, and "combined a cast-iron constitution with excellent moral qualities."[19]

After four and a half days of monotonous travel through almost level grassland, they entered the city of Córdoba, capital of the province of the same name. The city had about twenty thousand inhabitants, "mostly whites born there," and was situated near the Primero River at the foot of a mountain range, also called Córdoba. City officials and the governor of the province were most co-operative, providing information and donating natural history items to the Spanish commission. The naturalists made a six-day excursion into the mountains near Córdoba, enjoying the cool air and returning with many unusual plants and birds.[20]

Stagecoach travel was not suited to their needs since stops were not of their own choosing, so the commissioners decided to buy a coach and make their own arrangements for horses and drivers. The military escort continued with them for the next four hundred miles to Mendoza, with a change of personnel along the way. The most dangerous part of the trip was the section from Córdoba to Río

[19] Almagro, *Breve*, 24–25.
[20] *Ibid.*, 26; Isern letter II.

Cuarto, traversed by the naturalists the last three days of February, 1863. This region was feared because wild Pampas Indians frequently came from their villages as far as three hundred miles to the south, stealing cattle, killing men, and carrying off women and children. The Spaniards had no trouble, but there was a raid a few nights after they passed.[21]

From Río Cuarto, "a town of two to three thousand that doesn't have the least importance," the group went to Mendoza by way of San Luis. Their travel time was ten days, not counting six days spent on a hunting trip near San Luis. Here they bagged two *marras* or pampas hares (*Dolichotis patagonica*) and sent them to Madrid as the first ever imported to Europe.[22]

The old city of Mendoza, Argentina, located in a fertile valley where the pampas meet the Andes and on the main line of communication with Chile, had prospered down to the 1860's. Its population was about twenty thousand in March, 1861, when suddenly a terrible earthquake completely destroyed the city, burying two-thirds of the inhabitants in the debris. Fires swept through the devastated town, and the tilted land forced rivers and canals out of their banks, causing a flood. When Isern came upon the ruins two years later, he was "shocked at the sight of the drama; of the old city not one building was left intact." About a dozen small wooden store buildings had been built on the edge of the old settlement, but there was no church or any government edifice. At an open air memorial Mass the Spanish naturalists met the governor of Mendoza Province, who invited and accompanied them to his hacienda forty miles away. Besides hunting for specimens, they had the opportunity to examine some large crevices created by the earthquake.[23]

Since highway conditions over the Andes made travel by carriage impossible, the Iberians made arrangements to cross the mountains on horseback. The rugged crossing took six days as they climbed ten thousand feet to the pass, then back down to the Chilean town of

---

[21] Almagro, *Breve*, 26; Isern letter II.
[22] *Ibid.*; Almagro, *Breve*, 27.
[23] Isern letter II; Almagro, *Breve*, 27–28.

Los Andes. Besides horses, their caravan included pack mules and mounts for the mule driver and his assistants—twenty mules in all. The *madrina*, or lead mule, ridden by a ten-year-old boy, had a bell around her neck. At night they tied her up, and the others did not go far away.[24]

Hoping to cross in the cool of evening a hot sandy area about thirty miles wide, the group left Mendoza in late afternoon on the last day of March. As a gracious farewell gesture the governor and some fifty townspeople rode alongside them for about five miles. Riding all night, the naturalists and their retinue went beyond the sandy ground and began to climb through the mountain defiles. The following morning after a four-hour rest they continued the ascent, arriving at Uspallata at midnight. This Argentine establishment, about six thousand feet above sea level, "consisted of one half-destroyed building which served as the customs house." On April 2 they passed along the *laderas*, narrow roadways only a yard wide, cut into the mountains with rock on one side and a precipice on the other. There were four *laderas* along this highway, one of them a thousand yards long. Travelers continually sounded their horns to keep opposite-bound traffic from entering the narrow roadways, for it would be impossible to turn around and extremely difficult to back animals out if they met on the trail.[25]

Puente del Inca, the famous natural rock bridge, was the most enchanting spot on the Andean crossing. The Spaniards camped almost under it near some hot springs where water temperature varied from "warm to eighty-eight degrees" (Farenheit). After sampling the thermal waters, Almagro said, "The most sumptuous of the Roman emperors could not have taken a bath as delightful as ours, viewing the sublime cordillera under a haughty and picturesque natural bridge." Near by was snow-capped Aconcagua, the highest peak in the Western Hemisphere, rising 23,000 feet above the sea. They spent the afternoon collecting insects, herbs, and rocks while studying the peculiar ecology of the region. In the evening a group of guanaco (*Lama guanicoe*) hunters who were camped in the same place enter-

[24] *Ibid.*, 29.  [25] *Ibid.*, 29–30.

tained the Spaniards with Andean folklore. When the sun went down, it became so cold that their drinking water froze by eight o'clock, the temperature later dropping to twenty-one degrees.[26]

Around midday of Easter Sunday, 1863, the travelers crossed from Argentina into Chile at Uspallata Pass, 12,650 feet above sea level. Their descent toward the Pacific was rapid, the scenery changing from alpine to well-cultivated fields of maize and barley. On April 6 they reached the town of Santa Rosa de los Andes, where they left the mule team and rested before continuing the trip.[27]

Writing about the overland journey, Almagro noted that he and his companions had crossed the South American continent approximately along the thirty-third parallel of latitude. November to May, summer and fall in that hemisphere, were the prime months for trans-Andean crossings, when more than twenty thousand head of cattle were driven westward over the pass to Chile. In the opposite direction mule trains transported European goods from Chilean ports to interior provinces of Argentina. Snow closed the pass in winter except for biweekly mail service carried by men on snowshoes and skis. The Spanish anthropologist Almagro, born and raised on a Caribbean island, was profoundly impressed by the Andes Mountains, as his comments about the crossing show:

> An artist or scientist finds great interest in such a trip: the first admires the thousand natural beauties, capricious and varied landscapes, surprising by their sublimity, and splendid panoramas which nature formed in these gigantic mountains; the second is enabled to study stratification of rocks, beautiful porphyry, granite, basalt, quartz, and limestone, which, depending on elevation and topography, support soil where vegetation declines with altitude until it disappears altogether. One is astonished that some human beings choose their permanent home in such inhospitable regions, and one admires their ancestors who succeeded in opening roads where nature rebuffed them.[28]

[26] *Ibid.*, 30–32; Isern letter II.
[27] Almagro, *Breve*, 32–34.
[28] *Ibid.*, 33–34.

After several weeks' rest at the town of Los Andes, the Spanish naturalists continued their trek across Chile. Boxing up their animal, vegetable, and mineral specimens, they took a carriage to "the miserable village of Llay-Llay," where they boarded a train for Santiago, capital of the republic. Toward the end of April, 1863, they moved on to Valparaíso, Chile's principal seaport, where they were to meet the rest of the scientific commission and the naval squadron.[29]

[29] Isern letter II; Almagro, *Breve*, 34.

# VI

# Through the Strait and Around the Cape


W HILE FOUR of the Spanish scientists went overland to Chile, the others made the long voyage by sea. Leaving Montevideo in the middle of January, 1863, the Iberian frigates did not arrive in Valparaíso until the following May. In the interim they visited various ports and bays in the Strait of Magellan and the Falkland Islands, rounded Cape Horn, and anchored at some stations in southern Chile.

Marcos Espada traveled aboard the *Covadonga* where he received cordial treatment, even sharing the stateroom of his friend Captain Luis Fery. Espada always dined with the captain, and the two often played chess or discussed literary and scientific topics in the evenings.[1] But on the *Triunfo* the other members of the scientific commission were not so fortunate; the officers of that ship would not permit the civilian passengers to eat in their dining room. A note in Martinez' diary elaborates:

> We ate in my stateroom (not having another place to do it) as best we could since we lacked dishes and silver. When we separated messes, we were told that we could use the dishes, etcetera, and we counted on that, but only a few broken ones are begrudgingly loaned us each day.[2]

Fog and rough weather marked the three-week cruise to the Strait of Magellan. Espada and Martínez recorded in their diaries observations on phosphorescence in the water, sightings of birds, fish, seals, whales, and other ships. On calm days small boats were put out to fish and shoot birds. Occasionally Martínez fished from the porthole

---

[1] Jiménez de la Espada, *Diario*, 64.
[2] Martínez, *"Diario,"* Jan. 16, 1863, AMCN.

in his cabin. Espada's comments about shipboard activities reflect Spanish naval practices such as reading the penal code to the assembled crew. There was also a public sale of the personal effects of three sailors who jumped ship in Uruguay. "The quartermaster held up the objects; the sailors shouted out a price for them; midshipman Garay kept the records. The amount received goes to the government."[3]

Espada also observed and commented on the live animals carried aboard the *Covadonga*. In addition to pigs, chickens, and ducks, the menagerie included a dog named Czar and a cat. The young chickens got seasick, but the older ones learned how to take the rolling movement of the ship. The cat was a good sailor, while "Czar studied perfectly how to follow the different positions of sails for various maneuvers always placing himself in the best location."[4]

The first anchorage was just inside the Atlantic entrance to the Strait of Magellan at Possession Bay (Bahía Posesión), reached by the frigates on February 6 and the schooner six days later. High winds near the entrance of the Straits delayed the *Covadonga*, but Espada took advantage of the bad sailing weather to go ashore at Cabo Vírgenes. He described this part of the Patagonian coast as being flat and almost at sea level, with scanty vegetation, no trees or tall grass, and only a few cypress-like shrubs. There were cereals resembling rye and oats and some flowering plants, and sea shells, whale bones and skeletons of birds of prey littered the beach. Sea gulls were "without exaggeration like a cloud of mosquitoes . . . the noise of the wind and screech of marine birds are characteristic of this sad and infertile land."[5]

After a shouted salute of "Long live the Queen!" the ships left Bahía Posesión for Punta Arenas. Passing close to Tierra del Fuego, the large island on their left, Espada noted that it had "taller vegetation than Patagonia, bushes and low trees . . . its conical mountains,

---

[3] Jiménez de la Espada, *Diario*, 65, 72; Martínez, "*Diario*," Jan. 19, Feb. 2, 1863, AMCN.

[4] Jiménez de la Espada, *Diario*, 69.

[5] *Ibid.*, 75–79.

one against the other, more pointed than those of Patagonia."[6] It was night when they anchored at Punta Arenas, and in the darkness the *Triunfo* hit bottom and was temporarily stuck there. The Spanish ships used English sea charts "with the depths indubitably erroneously indicated," according to Espada.[7]

Punta Arenas was a Chilean military colony governed by a German, Herr George Scythe. The base was established in 1851 to assure Chilean control of the area, disputed with Argentina, and to serve as a center of trade and communication for the many neighboring Patagonian Indians. Fresh water and firewood were abundant at the sandy anchorage. Patagonian Indians had murdered the first governor, which explained why Colonel Scythe ruled the colony with an iron hand.

The Chilean settlement was composed of two hundred soldiers and their families, totaling about seven hundred people, who lived in rustic wooden houses. They were given daily rations: "two ounces of salted meat, half a pound of rice, another half pound of flour, the same of beans, some salt and chile peppers."[8] Each colonist received a whole ration. His family members got half that amount, except for children under one year, who got nothing. The governor's salary was two hundred pesos monthly; the physician earned seventy, the chaplain fifty, and a quartermaster thirty. The governor had a monopoly on all commercial activity. His principal income came from trading alcohol to the Indians for ostrich and guanaco skins. At a rate of from four to six bottles of *aguardiente* for one skin, Espada calculated that the governor had made 300,000 pesos in seven years of bartering. Except for the governor, alcohol was strictly prohibited in the colony itself. Colonel Scythe invited the Spanish naturalists to his home, where he presented them with some local items: an ostrich egg, deer antlers, animal skins, and thirteen species of mollusks.[9]

[6] *Ibid.*, 82.

[7] *Ibid.*, 80, 83.

[8] "*Diario de la fragata* Resolución," MS 808, fol. 10, Museo Naval, Madrid; hereafter referred to as MS 808, MN.

[9] *Ibid.*; Martínez, "*Diario*," Feb. 14, 1863, AMCN; Jiménez de la Espada, *Diario*, p. 83.

Soon after the Spanish ships docked at the colony, a number of nomadic Patagonian Indians arrived and pitched camp near by. Modest and tractable, some of the Indians spoke a little Spanish and English as well as their native tongue. They were tall and robust— Governor Scythe had measured three hundred males, finding an average height of six feet, three and three-eighths inches. The women were proportionally tall. All had abundant black hair, the women usually braiding theirs, the men often tying their long hair with a cord or scarf. They wore large capes of guanaco or ostrich skins which covered them from shoulders to ankles; some wore skirts or ponchos underneath. Their leather boots were made from the skin of horses' legs. Jewelry consisted primarily of shell or glass bead necklaces. Patagonians were good horsemen; they wore wooden spurs, used small saddles, and hunted with bola or bow and arrow. One characteristic that all the Spaniards noticed was the Indians' craving for alcoholic beverages. Espada saw a pretty young girl "stretched out on the beach, drunk and intoning a monotonous song." Later he saw the same girl drinking with a group of Indians in the chief's shack, where they passed a dented tin container around until all the liquor was gone. When the party broke up, the Patagonians staggered away singing, as they always did when drunk.[10]

Before leaving Punta Arenas the naturalists got permission to hunt in the adjacent forest. Guided by a military escort, they brought back plants, insects, and bird specimens, including varieties of gulls and small parrots. On boarding the *Triunfo*, Martínez encountered some Patagonian Indian chiefs "whom the captain had gotten drunk." Meanwhile, Espada bartered with another Indian, trading his blue necktie for one wooden spur.[11]

Early in the morning of February 15 the expedition sailed on toward Puerto del Hambre, famous in the annals of the Straits. Here the Spanish conquistador, Pedro Sarmiento de Gamboa, established a colony in the sixteenth century, but he was captured by the English and most of his men starved to death. A Chilean penal colony was set

[10] *Ibid.*, 83–85; MS 808, MN.
[11] Martínez, "*Diario*," Feb. 14, 1863, AMCN; Jiménez de la Espada, *Diario*, 85.

up in the same site in 1846. Four years later the hundred prisoners rebelled, killing the governor, chaplain, and other officials before they were subdued. The establishment was then transferred to Punta Arenas, garrisoned by voluntary soldiers rather than prisoners. When the naturalists arrived at Puerto del Hambre in 1863, they saw remains of wooden barracks and other vestiges of the hapless settlement.[12]

Puerto del Hambre was one of the most picturesque spots in the Straits, according to Espada. While anchored there, the ships' crews bathed in the surf, viewing in the distant background forests and snow-covered mountains. Heavy annual rainfall in the jagged terrain created fresh-water lakes and rivers, where deer, ducks, plovers, parrots, and other birds gathered. Once when Espada was collecting specimens in a small boat, he saw six Indians in a canoe, but the natives fled when they saw him, the two women rowing and their men watching. That night Espada wrote in his diary:

> Could they fear my gruff appearance as an armed hunter? Everything is possible, and I believe that this was one of the moments in which my pride as a civilized man manifested itself against those savages.[13]

Storms with extremely high winds, rain, and fog impeded the expedition's passage through the Strait. Finally, after a meeting of officers aboard the flagship on February 20, Admiral Pinzón ordered the two frigates to reverse their course and proceed around Cape Horn, stopping along the way at the Falkland Islands. Meanwhile, the schooner would wait out the storm, continue through the Straits, and rendezvous with the two frigates and the overland party in Valparaíso, Chile. "They villainously abandoned us in the Straits," wrote Espada, "leaving us alone against weather they did not dare face." While aboard the *Triunfo*, Martínez commented, "Our captain has more fear than shame."[14]

For the next two and a half weeks the *Covadonga* advanced and

[12] Account of 1850 revolt in MS 808, MN.
[13] Jiménez de la Espada, *Diario*, 88–89.
[14] *Ibid.*, 91; Martínez, "*Diario*," Feb. 20, 1863, AMCN.

retreated against strong winds and "the most terrible seas in the world," eventually reaching the calm Pacific Ocean. While passing Desolation Island, Espada observed that it merited the name, the bleak rocky coast being littered with "remains of shipwrecked boats, bottles, ironwork, etc."[15]

Their journey northward was uneventful except for a nine-day stop at Chiloé, a large island off the Chilean coast. The capital city, San Carlos de Ancud, was a town of about three thousand people, mostly Araucanian Indians. Espada said the natives were smaller than the Patagonians and dressed uniformly, the men in ponchos, the women in dark blue tunics, with a "hairy dull-brown square blanket." Some men earned their living by selling milk, others by loading coal from near-by deposits. They made their houses from *alera*, *cyna*, and *alerce*, local woods resembling pine. A week's sailing from Chiloé brought the Spanish schooner to Valparaíso, Chile, on March 28, about ten days ahead of the group going overland and six weeks ahead of the frigates.[16]

Aboard the *Triunfo*, Martínez recorded the adventures of his colleagues during the trip around Cape Horn, high-lighted by forty days in the Falkland Islands. Discovered in 1592, these islands, called Malvinas by the Spanish, had been successively claimed and colonized by Frenchmen, Spaniards, and Englishmen. Today England and Argentina both claim them, but the British flag flies over them as it did in 1863, when the Spanish expedition visited there. At that time the governor of the royal colony was an officer of the British Navy, Captain R. H. Mackenzie. On March 4, 1863, he came aboard the *Triunfo* to pay his respects to Captain Croquer, but unfortunately the latter was ashore. Martínez, obviously embarrassed, described the reception of the British officer, impeccably dressed in full uniform:

> The second in command took him to the captain's stateroom and offered him sherry wine. A sailor dressed in shirtsleeves, a red sash, and wooden sandals brought a bottle which had been opened previously and had a wooden plug in it, placing it on the table in front of

[15] Jiménez de la Espada, *Diario*, 95.
[16] *Ibid.*, 97.

the governor . . . . The cabin was dirty as usual; the Governor faced some dirty underwear and a soiled towel which hung near the washbasin.[17]

But Captain Mackenzie seemed to enjoy the visit and spoke in positive terms, praising some of the unusual swords he observed aboard the Spanish frigate.

The principal anchorage in the Falkland Islands was adjacent to the small town of Stanley, which had no hotel or restaurant. Most of the houses were one-story wooden structures with small individual gardens, and the church was "a house which had been fixed up for that purpose." The governor's residence was larger and set apart from the rest, as was a wooden warehouse full of supplies for the colony and trade items for England. Several residents of Stanley invited the Spanish naturalists to their homes; others provided boats or assistance. Charles Bull, Protestant chaplain of the colony, showed them his collection of fossils, rare minerals, antlers of Patagonian deer, guanaco skins, and a hothouse of European plants. Another interesting islander was consul of the United States of America, W. H. Smyley, who told them in Spanish about his more than eighty trips through the Strait of Magellan. Smyley, who had "made his fortune with some whaling ships," furnished horses and accompanied Puig and Martínez on a reconnaissance of the major island. A French fisherman and the Argentinian captain of a sealing vessel likewise shared knowledge and specimens with the Spaniards.[18]

It was not the best season for exploration; nevertheless, the naturalists did accumulate several crates of Falkland flora and fauna. Twenty penguins, several species of marine birds (including gulls and cranes), seals, fish, crustaceans, some unusual jellyfish, algae, mushrooms, shrubs, grasses, and grains are among items noted by Martínez.[19]

Living aboard a Spanish warship was difficult for the naturalists. Not only was working space at a minimum, but the civilians found

[17] Martínez, *"Diario,"* Mar. 4, 1863, AMCN.
[18] *Ibid.*, Mar. 1–4, 10, 1863, AMCN.
[19] *Ibid.*, Mar. 7, 9, 21, 1863, AMCN.

many naval regulations and practices onerous. Martínez, who was especially sensitive and devoutly religious, often was the only person attending Mass on the *Triunfo*, perhaps because the captain had announced several times to the crew that "as far as he was concerned, confession was not necessary." Martínez was also offended by the "barbarous and inhuman punishment" of a sailor, which all the crew had to watch. Even more repugnant were sodomy and homosexual practices, "more general than you would believe, especially among the officers who ought to have more education and morality."[20]

Sailing to Valparaíso, Chile, required one month, somewhat longer than the usual time because of storms followed by overly calm seas. As they were leaving the Falkland Islands, the two frigates collided, damaging guns, lifeboats, and porthole covers of both ships. The photographer's darkroom was made unusable. Water and wind drenched and whipped Martínez' cabin, forcing him to seek a dry place in the sailors' quarters. He was cheered by the good spirits of the young men in contrast to the perversity of the chief officers. Early in May when Martínez was dragging a fishing line from the deck, Captain Croquer sent orders for him to desist, citing naval regulations that prohibited the action. Martínez' angry reply was reserved for his diary:

> I can never believe that this rule refers to one who with moderation is trying to enrich the zoological collections of his country, exposing himself to public persecution by an ignorant and rebellious man.[21]

Finally on May 9, 1863, the Spanish frigates entered the Chilean port of Valparaíso, whereupon the naturalists went ashore at once for a joyful reunion with their colleagues of the scientific commission.[22]

[20] *Ibid.*, Mar. 16, 19, 20, 1863, AMCN.
[21] *Ibid.*, May 5, 1863, AMCN.
[22] *Ibid.*, April 10, 14, May 9, 1863, AMCN.

# VII

# Chilean Cities and Deserts

Headquarters for the Spanish naturalists in Valparaíso was the Hotel de l'Union, a two-story, tile-roofed structure near the center of town. Following a meeting of naval officers and scientists, the group decided to spend about a month in Chile, after which they would move north to Peru. Fernando Amor, who had come in the overland party, was already at work near Copiapó in the Atacama Desert studying the geologic and mineral formations and collecting specimens of copper, silver, gold, lead, iron, cobalt, and nickel. During his two-month field trip he also picked up a liver infection that sapped his strength, leading to his death later in the year.

Almagro compiled some data on Chilean population and economic life. He found that "almost all the European innovations," such as railroads, existed there and that "in the shadow of peace and order" commerce, agriculture, and mining were developing rapidly. Chile exported cereals to countries all around the Pacific Ocean; her fine wines, fruits, horses, and other agricultural products were sent to republics to the north; and minerals were in demand in Europe and North America. Valparaíso was a center for importation of European luxury goods, much of which was transshipped to Bolivia, Ecuador, Peru, and western Argentina. In 1863 the port city had about 70,000 inhabitants, "all white, the foreign element dominating, above all, the English."[1]

As in almost every city visited, local scientists and educated people of Valparaíso aided the commission members in their work. J. G. Plagemann, German head of a Chilean brewery, had a fine collection

[1] Almagro, *Breve*, 41–42.

of shells, zoophytes, minerals, plants, and Araucanian Indian artifacts. He introduced the Spaniards to cultured people, guided them
on collecting excursions, and donated some of his exhibition pieces to
the commission. One item he showed them was a mummified Indian
covered with brown clay, a preservation technique used by ancestors
of the Araucanians. Plagemann took them to the homes of upper-class
people, where Martínez remembered that they were "served tea or
chocolate; the señoritas are rather friendly and fond of playing the
piano." On May 13 the Philharmonic Society of Valparaíso gave a
splendid ball for the visiting Spaniards, where the dances included
quadrille, waltz, schottische, polka, and mazurka.[2]

Santiago, principal city and capital of Chile, was the next place on
the itinerary. The 120-mile trip from Valparaíso took fourteen hours
by stagecoach, with three changes of horses. Population of the capital
then was about 100,000; its notable landmarks included the presidential palace, cathedral, mint, theater, and buildings around the
main plaza. Situated in the Mopocho River valley near the base of the
Andes Mountains, Santiago was an exceptionally clean and modern
city with broad avenues and handsome plazas. Welcoming his compatriots to Chile, Señor Tavira, the Spanish minister, arranged a visit
for them to the home of the minister of foreign relations.[3]

Dr. Roel Philippi, a German immigrant who taught zoology and
botany at the university, headed Santiago's museum of natural history.
He and his German taxidermist-assistant had arranged impressive
exhibits of Chilean birds, mammals, reptiles, insects, minerals, and
plants. Martínez noted that the museum had a fine library of scientific
periodicals and books, dealing mostly with Chile. Herr Philippi had
published many articles about Chile in foreign journals, and the
Chilean government had just published his book about the Atacama
Desert. He expressed surprise at the lack of financial and logistic
support for the Spanish expedition, to which Martínez responded,
"Except for breathing we have had privations in everything, even

[2] Martínez, "*Diario*," May 11–13, 1863, AMCN.
[3] *Ibid.*, May 16, 18, 21, 1863, AMCN; Almagro, *Breve*, 42–43.

eating, because of the lack of care with which everything pertaining to this commission is done."[4] Philippi introduced the Spaniards to Frederick Leybold, a German botanist and pharmacist, who was about to publish a series of monographs on Chilean plants. "He has just finished *Violets*," wrote Martínez; "he draws very well."[5] Leybold also collected eggs, birds, reptiles, and skins of quadrupeds, which he sent to correspondents in Germany. He invited Martínez to join him in a guanaco hunt later in the month.

Philippi also took the visitors to the University of Chile, where he introduced them to the rector and various professors. Ignacio Domeyko, a Polish professor of mineralogy, headed the university. He had been in Chile for several years, had an intimate knowledge of the important mining regions, and had published a Spanish textbook on mineralogy. Other visits were made to the agricultural school, art gallery, national library, theater, Jesuit school, astronomical observatory, and topographical commission. A Frenchman headed the last, and a German was chief astronomer at the observatory.[6]

Excursions to the Chilean countryside interested the naturalists, especially botanist Isern. One trip by horseback took them to a dry lake, Quilicura; another journey took them to Lake Acubo, which was replete with ducks, swans, and other aquatic life. They stayed at Viluco hacienda, where, surrounded by beautiful gardens, the main complex had "large rooms, library, billiards, several chapels, fine servants' quarters." On other occasions they explored extensive stretches along the Mopocho River. Birds, insects, frogs, and plants were the principal items they collected, prepared, identified, and readied for shipment to Spain.[7]

Spanish residents of Santiago gave a gala banquet for the visitors on June 1. Guests included Admiral Pinzón and his squadron officers, the scientists, foreign diplomats, Chilean cabinet officers, and a number of university professors. Martínez left rather early, "since

---

[4] Martínez, "*Diario*," May 20, 1863, AMCN.
[5] *Ibid.*
[6] *Ibid.*, May 21–22, 28–29, 1863, AMCN.
[7] *Ibid.*, May 25–26, 31, 1863, AMCN.

wine was flowing too freely and too much to some." A few days later a ball was given in honor of the same group, but there must have been less wine since Martínez stayed until three-thirty in the morning.[8]

Returning to Valparaíso early in June, the commission members had an opportunity to do more collecting in the coastal region. For an overnight trip to the Bellavista hacienda they took a train to Quillota, where they were met by two señoritas, nieces of the owner, who accompanied them to the property. This was a magnificent estate, with lakes, forests, formal gardens, and a mansion with many servants. Very few times during the expedition would the naturalists enjoy accommodations like this on a field trip. Back in Valparaíso the beach and bay yielded interesting items for study, and the city itself provided unusual material of a social and historical nature. One novelty for the Spaniards was Valparaíso's modern fire-fighting unit. Its extension ladders and pump wagons impressed Martínez and were recorded on a film plate by the Spanish photographer.[9]

A fabulous farewell banquet in Valparaíso made the visiting Spaniards feel that they were witnessing a new era in friendly Ibero-American relations. Held in the patio of the Victoria Theater amid boxed trees and marble statues, the affair had elaborate decorations featuring two large arches, one dedicated to Queen Isabella I of Spain with the names of Columbus' three ships, the other for Queen Isabella II and the *Resolución, Triunfo*, and *Covadonga*. Flags, banners, and signs proclaimed liberty, fraternity, and faith, and commemorated the great Spanish *conquistadores*. Two orchestras, one from the Spanish flagship, provided music, which was interspersed with poetry and the usual toasts. One of the toasts ran thus:

> The learned man goes to unknown regions in search of truth, and if he completes his mission—if he doesn't lose his life for science in the savage jungle—he returns to his country where triumphal arches and monuments do not await him. Silent libraries and museums enriched by him receive the fruit of his work for the good of present

[8] *Ibid.*, June 1, 4, 1863, AMCN.
[9] *Ibid.*, June 7–8, 1863, AMCN; Rafael Castro y Ordóñez photograph collection, AMCN.

and future generations. Scientific Commission of the Pacific: complete your mission in Columbus' world, so rich and unexplored![10]

Before leaving Valparaíso, the scientists separated, Isern and Almagro heading for the highlands of Bolivia and Peru while the others continued north in the *Covadonga*. This ship's size and shallow draft permitted it to enter some of the smaller coves and ports on the Pacific coast; furthermore, the captain and crew were friendlier than those of the *Triunfo*. Amor, still at Copiapó in the Atacama Desert, would join the naturalists when they reached that mining center.

First stop for the *Covadonga* was Coquimbo, where anchor was dropped on June 13. High point of the naturalists' visit here was seeing the conch collection belonging to an elderly Englishman, Thomas Richardson. He "knew nothing about science," but with the help of an assistant had amassed an astonishing number of species from Chile, Peru, and the South Pacific. Many of the items were boxed because he was preparing to return to England, but he unpacked them and gave the Spaniards 742 mollusks representing 34 species. Richardson's wife had a small business trading for chinchilla skins; Martínez selected two from a group of over 2,000. The next day a short railroad trip to the mining center of La Serena yielded mineral specimens, and local fishermen were commissioned to assemble a variety of fish and marine life.[11]

Following a one-day stop in Huasco, the schooner sailed to Caldera, where it remained about ten days. From the ship's deck one could easily see that the land was pure desert: "here not even a shrub could be seen—not even grass. . . . fine white sand covered all the land as far as you could see in all directions."[12] Much of the town and wooden pier belonged to a copper mining company, as did a large smelter near by. The Spaniards planned to visit the center of mining at

[10] Banquet described in *El Eco del Pacífico*, San Francisco, Calif., Aug. 13, 1863, reprinted from *Mercurio* of Valparaíso, Chile.
[11] Martínez, *"Diario,"* June 13–16, 1863, AMCN; list of mollusks in Almagro, *Breve*, 164–66.
[12] Martínez, *"Diario,"* June 18, 1863, AMCN.

Chañarcillo and Copiapó, but they had to wait a day for the train. Meanwhile, they fished and dragged the bay, getting some good advice and specimens from a group of Italian immigrant fishermen.

Martínez said the three-hour train ride to Copiapó was like a trip over an immense sand dune. They found the mining center booming, its cultural life revolving around the theater and parties given by the several foreign consuls who resided there. Although he met a Spaniard who had just made a fortune in mining, Martínez observed that the mines "have created more poor than rich, and not a few Spaniards have lost in them fortunes acquired by hard work and economy in business."[13]

After a long talk with Amor about his two months' study of the region, Paz and Martínez walked around Copiapó. At the plaza they visited the main church and saw an "artistically poor" statue of Juan Godoy, discoverer of the rich mines of Chañarcillo. Built in a narrow valley, the town straddled a river full of brackish water used for irrigation and to drive water wheels for the smelter. Preliminary grinding of the copper ore was done with large stone wheels, a vertical one riding on a horizontal one, which worked on the minerals carried to the mill suspended in a stream of river water. An administrator showed the Spaniards through the smelter, after which he offered them a light lunch of bread, cheese, wine, and grapes. The naturalists received such fine treatment by their countrymen who lived in that remote area that one remarked, "The truest lovers of their country are outside of it."[14]

An eccentric spinster, Miss Teresa Gallo, owned the best private scientific collection in Copiapó. "Owing to family circumstances," she had retired from society, finding in natural history an absorbing interest that had made the years pass happily. The visiting naturalists were surprised by the quantity and impressed by the excellent preparation of her specimens of minerals, birds, mollusks, plants, and corals. She had a large aviary in the patio and many live plants growing in

[13] *Ibid.*, June 21–22, 1863, AMCN.
[14] *Ibid.*, June 19, 1863, AMCN.

well-marked plots. When she showed them a mummy of a Patagonian Indian boy, Martínez thought that somehow the look of fear on the mummy had been transferred to its owner.[15]

Returning to the port of Caldera via the mines of Chañarcillo, the Spaniards prepared for their next important stop at Cobija, Bolivia. This town, later conquered by Chile, proved to be another arid port important only for shipping minerals. On a side trip the naturalists went by horseback some miles inland to see the mine named El Toldo, where they descended into the pit itself. A windlass lifted the ore out of the mine; peons then carried it in leather sacks to a near-by area where the metals were extracted either by furnaces or the patio process. In the latter technique, mercury was used to form an amalgam with silver in the crushed ore, then the two metals were separated. Workers and officials at Chañarcillo lived in "miserable houses" near the mine, "the only things visible in this extremely arid region."[16]

Back in Cobija the Spanish vice-consul entertained the visitors in his home and agreed to forward their large collection of mineral specimens, among them a pure copper nugget weighing over one thousand pounds. He had already sent some Indian costumes and jewelry to Madrid for Almagro, who had passed through Cobija in mid-June.[17]

Arica was the first Peruvian port of call for the naturalist aboard the *Covadonga*. Arriving there on July 3, 1863, they were surprised by the great number of aquatic birds in the bay and the peculiar gray color of the landscape, caused by the heavy overlay of guano, or bird droppings. Rich in phosphates and nitrogenous matter, these deposits were mined and shipped in great quantities to Europe, where they were used to fertilize the exhausted soils. Looking for artifacts, Martínez walked to an ancient Indian burial ground and the contemporary cemetery. At the former site he saw fragments of pottery, clothing, and many skulls and human bones; at the latter, "between the wooden crosses, remains of household belongings of the dead such as mattresses, pillows, boxes, etcetera, mixed with garbage."[18]

[15] *Ibid.*, June 21, 1863, AMCN.
[16] *Ibid.*, July 1, 1863, AMCN.
[17] *Ibid.*                           [18] *Ibid.*, July 4, 6, 1863, AMCN.

Visiting the rocky promontory of Morro, the naturalists found it a refuge for pelicans, gulls, seals, and marine life. A natural cave yielded more items for their collection, while near by were burial sites of an ancient fishing people. The burial grounds had been disturbed by grave-diggers in search of buried treasure, who left the sandy dunes littered with skulls, bones, and fragments of pottery and textiles.[19]

A trip to the mining center of Tacna gave the Spaniards a view of the southern coastal region of Peru. Homes and buildings were built low with "distinctive roofs resembling coffins," but the visitors were pleased by the many Spanish architectural details, like wrought-iron grilles and balconies. A river bisected Tacna's central park, supplying water for irrigated land on the outskirts. The naturalists stayed in the Bola de Oro Hotel and attended the theater, where "the play was bad, the company of actors worse." The two-and-one-half-hour train trip to and from Tacna was summarized by Martínez: "There is little one can say about a railroad going through an immense desert with only a little shack for a station."[20]

From Arica the *Covadonga* sailed north to Callao, entrepôt for the capital city of Lima. Along the way the naturalists studied and prepared their specimens of fish, seals, birds, minerals, plants, and Indian artifacts. The items included coca leaves, a narcotic commonly used by the natives, and "ash rolls," a condiment prepared by burning thistle-like plants. When they docked at Callao on July 12, 1863, the two Spanish frigates were already in port.[21]

[19] *Ibid.*, July 4, 1863, AMCN.
[20] *Ibid.*, July 4–6, 1863, AMCN.
[21] *Ibid.*, July 6–12, 1863, AMCN.

# VIII

# Highlands of Bolivia and Peru

Wʜɪʟᴇ ᴍᴏsᴛ of the members of the Spanish scientific commission visited ports and mining centers along the Pacific coast of South America, the anthropologist and botanist traversed the highlands of Bolivia and Peru. Their two-and-one-half-month excursion was on foot and horse- or muleback, much of it at altitudes between ten and fourteen thousand feet in midwinter. Although Almagro and Isern suffered from the penalties of such a trip, both acknowledged the tremendous insight gained from their experience in the kingdom of the ancient Incas. They also were able to bring back information and specimens illustrating the natural history of that region.

Tacna, Peru, was the starting point for their ascent of the Andes. They reached this spot on June 18, 1863, having taken a coastal steamer from Valparaíso to Arica, then the railroad to Tacna. Preparing for the mountain journey, they assembled camping equipment, including blankets, cooking utensils, and food. Here too they secured the services of an expert guide and muleteer who promised to lead them to La Paz, Bolivia, 250 miles to the east and 12,000 feet above sea level.[1]

Riding mules, Almagro and Isern left Tacna on June 21 and spent the first four days in the mountains of southern Peru. On the second day they reached El Ingenio, a mining camp at eight thousand feet, where they experienced firsthand the altitude sickness called *soroche* or *veta* in Peru and Bolivia and *puna* in Chile. Symptoms of this infirmity are intense headache, dizziness, nausea, and difficulty in breathing. It is caused by the relative lack of oxygen in high mountain air. After an eighteen-hour rest they continued scaling the sharp inclines,

[1] Isern letter II.

struggling against a strong, cold wind. June 23 they stopped overnight at Tacora, a tambo, or mountain shelter, at the foot of the snow-
covered range of the same name. The squalid hovel had rock walls
"full of holes," providing little protection against the below-zero
temperature and hurricane-like winds. In a letter to a friend Isern
described tambos:

> These are huts in which one does not look for comfort: the bed is
> what the traveler brings; a filthy table, if any; sometimes a broken
> chair; the doorway is secured with a large stone. . . . At night the
> traveler has his *chupe* which is a stew of potatoes, meat, ají (hot
> peppers), and broth.[2]

Sometimes Indian families lived in these tambos; they invariably did
not speak Spanish.

Between the mountain ranges the Spaniards crossed altiplanos, or
high plains, where they saw large flocks of domesticated llamas, long-
haired alpacas, and wild vicuñas. The Quechua and Aymará Indians,
who tended these animals, were direct descendants of the ancient
Incas, and they preserved the old techniques of spinning and weaving
woolen cloth for blankets and wearing apparel. Highland Indian men
all wore handsome ponchos and woolen caps, and the women kept
warm and stylish with three or more brightly colored woolen skirts.

Late in the afternoon of June 24 the travelers waded across the
Mauri River, a boundary then between Peru and Bolivia. After a
short walk they decided to ask for refuge in an Indian shack along the
river. "Nothing was more repugnant," wrote Almagro, "than that
miserable doorless hut of piled-up rocks, only one room about fourteen feet square where we had to cook, eat, and sleep in the company
of the owner's family, consisting of six dirty individuals and a multitude of rabbits."[3]

Continuing along the high plains, frequently slipping and sliding
on the ice-covered trail, they came to the little Bolivian town of
Santiago de Machaca, where they stayed with the parish priest. On the

[2] *Ibid.*; Almagro, *Breve*, 44.
[3] *Ibid.*, 45.

twenty-sixth they found lodgings at Nazacara, a small settlement near the Desaguadero River, and the following day crossed that stream on a unique pontoon bridge formed by a series of reed canoes tied together. Following an overnight stop in Viacha, the mule train entered Bolivia's capital on June 28, having averaged about thirty-six miles a day for the previous seven days.[4]

During their nine days in La Paz the two naturalists stayed at the home of a Spanish businessman since there was no inn of any type in the city. Almagro assembled some data about the country and its capital. He found that in spite of being in the tropics, La Paz had a cold climate because of its elevation of almost 12,000 feet and its location near Illimani Peak, which rises to 21,185 feet above sea level. He estimated the capital's population at more than 50,000, but Isern thought it was nearer 85,000. Both agreed that the majority of the inhabitants were pure Aymará Indians. Chief Bolivian agricultural exports were quinine, coca leaves, chocolate, coffee, and sugar; and the famed Bolivian mines produced abundant quantities of silver, gold, tin, copper, and bismuth. Almagro's observations about the stratification of society parallel the following statement from a modern encyclopedia regarding Bolivia: "Broadly speaking the whites are landowners and government officials; mestizos are tradesmen, skilled workers, and minor civil servants; and the Indians laborers."[5]

Botanizing near La Paz, Isern found several species of *Mutisia*, a South American climbing shrub, and many varieties of potatoes. Since the high altitude of Bolivia's population clusters precluded growing corn or wheat, the Indians depended on potatoes or *oca* (*Oxalis tuberosa*) and quinoa (*Chenopodium quinoa*), native food plants that withstood the climate and elevation.[6]

Two fiestas climaxed the naturalists' visit to Bolivia. First a group of Franciscan monks, the majority of whom were Spaniards, gave a

[4] *Ibid.*, 45–46.

[5] "Bolivia," *Encyclopaedia Britannica*, III, 815; Isern letter II; Almagro, *Breve*, 46–47.

[6] Isern to Mariano Paz Graells, La Paz, Bolivia, June 30, 1863, Barreiro, *Historia*, 178.

A colonial arcade at Santiago de Chile, June, 1863.

The Cathedral (Iglesia Matriz), Santiago de Chile, June, 1863.

A railroad train to a copper mine, Chañarcillo, Chile, June, 1863.

A copper mine at Chañarcillo, June, 1863.

Indian miners at Chañarcillo, June, 1863.

The gate to Callao, Lima, Peru, July, 1863.

The port of Callao, July, 1863.

A stone bridge over the Rimac River, Lima, July, 1863.

The Cathedral at Lima, July, 1863.

Torre Tagle palace at Lima, July, 1863.

The Columbus statue, Lima, July, 1863.

The Bolívar memorial, Plaza de Inquisición, Lima, July, 1863.

Presa palace, Lima, July, 1863.

A secondary school at Pisagua, Peru (now Chile), June, 1863.

Native shacks near Chorrillos, Peru, July, 1863.

The Cathedral, Panama City, August, 1863.

dinner for the visitors during which the monastery rang out with *"vivas"* for Spain, Queen Isabella II, the Spanish expedition, and the growth of the Roman Catholic missions. More exciting was the annual celebration in honor of San Pedro, when thousands of masked and costumed Indians danced in the streets and plazas of La Paz.[7]

Leaving Bolivia's capital on July 6, the two men headed for Tiahuanaco, one of the major archaeological sites of South America. Only forty miles from La Paz, this small town was once the seat of a flowering pre-Inca civilization, survived by the artistic remains of statues, pillars, monoliths, stone sculpture, and the famous Gateway of the Sun. Fascinated by these, Almagro wrote, "We saw impressive low reliefs carved in hard polished sandstone and cut stones so colossal that one was twenty-six feet long, thirteen feet wide, and five feet thick."[8] The quarry for these worked blocks of stone was fifteen miles away. Since the natives did not have iron tools, large beasts of burden, or the concept of the wheel, their construction seemed all the more remarkable.

During their ten days in Tiahuanaco, prolonged by Almagro's illness, the Spaniards lived in an adobe hut "full of holes and with a cowhide for a door." The elevation of almost two and a half miles along with cold winds and snow forced them to wear all the clothing they could, while at night they covered themselves with sweaty horse blankets. Since no one in the town spoke Castilian, communication was almost impossible; but the visitors were able to secure essential items: water, firewood, potatoes, and dried meat.[9]

Isern scoured the neighboring area for plants, while Almagro excavated ancient graves, called chulpas by the Aymará Indians. In addition to skeletons he found artifacts of clay, stone, silver, gold, copper, and a mixture of the last two called *tumbaga*. The pre-Inca skulls that Almagro sent back to Spain sloped noticeably from front to back, and he said that this shape was caused by slant boards purposely applied to infants' heads.[10]

---

[7] Almagro, *Breve*, 48; Barreiro, *Historia*, 178.
[8] Almagro, *Breve*, 48.
[9] *Ibid.*, 49.                    [10] *Ibid.*

From Tiahuanaco, Almagro and Isern moved north to the town of Guaqui on Lake Titicaca, highest navigable lake in the world. About 138 miles long and 70 miles wide, this lake was the womb of Inca Indian mythology, the first gods having risen out of the sacred water. It was also the boundary between Bolivia and Peru. The scenery was spectacular, with high, snowy mountains surrounding the island-dotted lake on which colorfully dressed Indians paddled in their straw or reed canoes "of difficult equilibrium." Almagro noted that the Peruvian government was at that time engaged in bringing the first steamboats to the lake "to give life to its handsome and desert margins."[11]

Their next important stop was Puno, Peru, at the other end of Lake Titicaca, which they reached on July 21. A provincial capital of eight thousand people, Puno was equally famous for its mines and its Indian dances. Here Almagro and Isern decided to separate, the anthropologist heading for Cuzco, famous capital of the Incas, while the botanist visited Arequipa and southern Peru. They promised to reunite in Lima, Peru's capital, in a month or so. One consideration leading to the split was the difficulty of securing five mules, which they needed for themselves and their growing collection of skulls, artifacts, minerals, and plant specimens. Such a large mule train would be a target for bandits, they were advised.[12]

Isern and a muleteer left Puno with most of the collection on July 27. It took eight days of difficult travel to reach the lovely city of Arequipa, the regional capital noted for its healthful climate. Here the botanist visited famed El Misti Volcano and marveled at the colonial architecture with elaborate façades carved from white sillar stone. After acquiring abundant plant specimens, he headed for the port of Islay, a trip involving a ninety-mile journey across a barren desert. He traveled the last leg of the trip aboard a coastal steamer from Islay to Callao, Lima's port, where he arrived on August 23, 1863.[13]

Meanwhile, Almagro began his long overland trek to Lima by way

[11] *Ibid.*, 50.
[12] *Ibid.*, 50–51.
[13] Isern letter II; Almagro, *Breve*, 51.

of Cuzco and other cities of the sierra. Leaving Puno on July 27, he first visited a site called Cilostani, where there were pre-Spanish ruins of tall stone towers marking tombs of an ancient people. The following night he slept in Pucará, having passed through the Indian villages of Hatuncoya and Lampa. Continuing along the *páramo* or high plateau, at an average speed of forty-five miles a day, he passed through Sicuani and Urcos and arrived in Cuzco on the last day of July. The prefect of that province, an army general, took Almagro into his home and served as his guide for the next twelve days.[14]

Center of the Inca empire and known by Quechua-speaking Indians as "navel of the world," Cuzco has long been a mecca for anthropologists and students of Andean civilizations. In spite of earthquakes and destructive forces of time and man, this city still boasts temples, walls, fortresses, and other remains of a highly developed Indian society. Almagro called it the "Athens of the Incas," cradle of their culture. He visited the ancient Temple of the Sun, over which a Dominican convent had been superimposed, and noted that another convent (Santa Catalina) was formerly a sumptuous residence for the Inca's concubines. "A great part of the present city is built on foundations of large burnished stones fitted artistically together so perfectly you cannot insert a needle in the joints."[15]

Cuzco, a city of about 25,000 people in 1863, also had notable architectural and historical remnants from the Spanish colonial period. "The cathedral of Cuzco is a stately monument," wrote Almagro, "capable of competing with the most beautiful of Europe, and certainly the best in South America."[16] Built in the sixteenth century, its main altar was of pure silver. Other treasures included precious stones, magnificent jewelry, and excellent antique oil paintings. The Jesuit church on the main plaza was another fine example of rich baroque architecture. The plaza itself had been the setting for famous coronations, executions, and other pageantry.

Outside the city but near by were a number of historical monu-

[14] *Ibid.*, 50–52.
[15] *Ibid.*, 52.
[16] *Ibid.*, 53.

ments or sites. Almagro called the Inca fortress of Sacsahuamán overlooking Cuzco "magnificent," and he walked to the battlefield of Salinas, where a sixteenth-century Almagro was defeated by the forces of Pizarro in the civil war between Peru's conquerors. Digging around in ruins, the Spanish anthropologist found pottery and stone artifacts but was unable to take larger items to Lima, six hundred miles away.[17]

On horseback and with a pack mule Almagro left Cuzco August 11, accompanied by an Indian guide who preferred to walk. They traveled along the picturesque Urubamba River valley, sleeping the first night in Urubamba and the second in Ollantaytambo. At the latter place Almagro inspected lofty Inca stone ruins on a hill two thousand feet above the river, and saw for the first time an Inca suspension bridge with cables made of twisted vines. Although the vines swayed in the breeze, the animals passed easily over the bridge, since they were accustomed to it.[18]

Ayacucho was Almagro's next destination. The trip took a week across mountains, valleys, and rivers, the two men staying in thatched or adobe huts. In the Spanish colonial period Ayacucho was called Huamanga, but following Peru's war of independence the city received the name of the final decisive battle fought about twelve miles out of town. Almagro visited the battlefield on August 22, remaining overnight at a near-by settlement.[19]

A few days later he was in Huancayo, important trade center for the rich Jauja Valley. Almagro, fatigued by two months of rigorous high mountain travel, found it a delightful place, with its green fields, fruit trees, several rivers, majestic mountains, and white buildings. The valley measured about twenty by forty miles, and in spite of being two miles above sea level, its proximity to the Equator gave it a delightful climate, favorable to cultivation of temperate-zone products. Huancayo was then famous, as it still is, for its weekly market, where hundreds of Indians come to exchange their produce and handicrafts.[20]

The distance from Huancayo to Lima was about 130 miles, which

[17] *Ibid.*, 53–55.
[19] *Ibid.*, 56.
[18] *Ibid.*, 55–56.
[20] *Ibid.*, 57–58.

Almagro covered in four days. He crossed the Oroya River on a bridge made of willows and had to traverse the Morococha Mountains through a pass three miles above sea level. For the last part of the trip he followed the Rímac River all the way to Lima, where he arrived on August 30, "so dissipated, poorly dressed, and listless after a trip on horseback of 1,350 miles through mountains and wilderness that they did not want to accept him in the hotel."[21] He stayed a few days at the home of the Spanish vice-consul in Lima, enjoying the luxuries of white sheets on the bed and delicious food.

From the vice-consul, Almagro and Isern learned that Admiral Pinzón and the Spanish squadron had visited Lima in July, but had sailed on to Panama and California. Pinzón had left them some money, and the president of the scientific commission had left a sealed communication in which he ordered them to carry out further investigations in the interior of Peru. They were to join the Spanish squadron in mid-November, when it returned to Callao.[22]

[21] *Ibid.*, 58.
[22] Barreiro, *Historia*, 208.

# IX

# Lima, Guayaquil, and Panama City

WHEN ADMIRAL PINZÓN's Spanish squadron anchored in Callao, Peru, on July 11, 1863, they received a tremendous reception. That evening a launch decorated with colored lanterns and carrying an orchestra and a theatrical music company (zarzuela) serenaded the visitors for almost two hours. From the frigates there were *"vivas"* for Peru and Spain, while the flagship's band played the anthems of Spain, *"Himno de Riego,"* and Peru, *"Marcha Real."* A leading newspaper, *El Comercio,* published a seventeen-stanza poem dedicated to the Spaniards and their safe arrival in Peru.[1]

Since the *Covadonga,* carrying the naturalists, arrived in Callao a day later, they missed the gala port reception, but were feted in Lima. Going the eight miles to Lima by train, they took rooms at Morin's Warm Bath Hotel on the Plaza de Armas, or main square, of Peru's capital. In Martínez' diary there is a business card from the hotel proclaiming in English, "This great establishment presents to strangers every convenience that may be desired . . . billiards, shooting gallery . . . seven languages are spoken in the Establishment."[2]

Lima, founded in 1535 by Francisco Pizarro, got its name from a corruption of "Rímac," which is the name of the river flowing through that population center. The capital is also known as the City of Kings, since its site was chosen on January 6, feast day of the Wise Men, or Three Kings. In 1863 its population exceeded 100,000, according to Manuel Almagro, who attempted to ascertain such statistics in each place the scientists visited. He noted that most of the buildings looked wretched from the outside, but many had luxuriously decorated in-

[1] *El Comercio,* Lima, July 11, 1863.
[2] Martínez, *"Diario,"* July 12, 1863, AMCN.

teriors. The streets were straight, wide, horribly paved, and in general very dirty because of the open sewers in the middle of each one.

That which constitutes the pleasantness of Lima and has produced the fame it enjoys is its fine society, as hospitable as it is charming. . . . The female of Lima is the essence of amiability, fineness, and high tone: a vivacious talent, prodigious intelligence, lively and spirited imagination, which makes relations with pretty Lima girls highly pleasing.[3]

It surprised and impressed the Spanish naturalists that Lima's government buildings, with the exception of a new penitentiary, were all built by Spaniards in colonial days. The main plaza was like an architectural museum, preserving the past in general appearance and specific detail. Pizarro's palace still stood there, serving as presidential mansion, while across the way the impressive cathedral and adjacent archbishop's palace appeared unchanged from the days of the early viceroys. Even the handsome bronze fountain in the center of the plaza had been spouting water for over two centuries. Near by the Peruvian Legislature met in a Spanish baroque building, formerly a Jesuit school, and venerable San Marcos University occupied buildings as old as its sixteenth-century charter.

For several days the Spaniards walked around Lima observing notable buildings and monuments and met with Peruvians who had a professional interest in science. Comments in their journals refer to the Dominican convent, a recently erected statue of Columbus, the theater where they saw a performance of *Norma*, and the museum of natural science. At the latter they found a conglomorate of minerals, birds, insects, mollusks, fossils, mummies, coffins, clocks, portraits of Spanish viceroys, Indian relics, animal monstrosities, "all badly cared for, displayed, and dirty."[4]

Antonio Raimondi was one of the important Peruvian naturalists who played host to the visiting Iberians. Each year at government expense he spent several months exploring regions of Peru and

[3] Almagro, *Breve*, 67.
[4] Martínez, "*Diario*," July 13, 1863, AMCN; Almagro, *Breve*, 66–67.

gathering data and specimens. Accompanying the Spaniards on a tour of the medical school and hospital, he was able to introduce them to several Peruvian scientists. Martínez said that Raimondi's private collection and that of a man named Davila were superior to those of any Peruvian museum. He was also impressed by the rich collection of huacos, or ancient Indian pots, and other items belonging to Señor Ferreiros, director of public instruction.[5]

In the outskirts of Lima the Spanish naturalists located, studied, and collected some items of natural history. Near Chorrillos, a beach resort nine miles from the capital, they found insects under rocks, mollusks, and marine life. It was midwinter, which meant that much vegetation was dormant; but since the climate was benign and the temperature rarely fell below 45 degrees, plants were abundant. Public markets were another commonly tapped source for unusual specimens, but cost and the uncertainty of provenance were serious drawbacks. Cemeteries, they discovered, often had extensive varieties of trees, shrubs, and flowering plants. While visiting Lima's cemetery the Spaniards were shocked to see a stack of coffins ready for cremation, for they were accustomed to ground or vault burial.[6]

After two weeks in the Lima area the Spanish squadron moved north to Ecuador, missing the excitement and fun of Peru's independence day, July 28. But that was by design, since Admiral Pinzón's orders specified that his ships were to avoid trouble by being absent from any Latin-American republic during holidays commemorating victories over Spain. Almagro and Isern were still in the highlands of Peru, and the president of the scientific commission remained in Lima; but the other five Spanish naturalists went aboard the *Triunfo* before sailing time on July 26.

The continuing dispute between Captain Croquer of the *Triunfo* and President Paz of the scientific commission came to a head at this time. When Paz left the frigate in Montevideo, preferring to go overland to Chile, then switched his group to the *Covadonga* for the trip to Peru, Croquer judged that the scientists had left his ship for

[5] Martínez, "*Diario*," July 14, 21, 1863, AMCN.
[6] Barreiro, *Historia*, 190.

good. He ordered their staterooms to be cleared out, breaking the lock on Paz's dresser, according to a complaint filed in Callao on July 15 by the head naturalist. Admiral Pinzón ordered an official inquiry, appointing a board of naval officers to investigate the charges. They voted discontinuance, and the case passed to the naval advisory board, which censured the captain's conduct. Meanwhile, Paz decided to resign his post and return to Spain by commercial ship. On July 24 he turned over all official correspondence to Martínez, who became the new head of the Scientific Commission of the Pacific.[7] Amor, as vice-president of the commission, should have succeeded Paz, but his serious illness prevented his doing so.

Stopping briefly in the port of Paita, Peru, the *Triunfo* sailed to the Gulf of Guayaquil, Ecuador, anchoring at Puná Island on August 2, 1863. The following day the naturalists boarded a shallow-draft schooner for the four-hour trip to Guayaquil. Although it is Ecuador's principal port, the city is located forty miles from the Pacific coast on the Guayas River. This river is salty and affected by ocean tides for more than eighty miles from its mouth. For six hours the water runs toward the ocean, then it reverses for the next six hours. Navigation by rafts and small boats takes advantage of this phenomenon.[8]

From the river, Guayaquil looked attractive, but once in the town the Spaniards found it to be dirty, with burros, chickens, and pigs wandering loose in the streets. One of the naturalists estimated the population at 20,000, "composed of Negroes, mulattoes, Indians, and whites." The buildings, many of wood with thatched roofs, were old and mud stained; there were foul swamps near by; poverty was widespread; the unpaved streets were either "quagmires or dustbins," depending on the weather. Almagro's criticism of the city concluded:

> Add to these circumstances a suffocating and high temperature, frequent and heavy rains during six months, an enormous plague of all kinds of offensive insects, and you will comprehend that Guayaquil is one of the most disagreeable cities in the world.[9]

[7] Martínez, *"Diario,"* July 23–24, 1863, AMCN; Barreiro, *Historia,* 188.
[8] Martínez, *"Diario,"* July 30–Aug. 4, 1863, AMCN; Almagro, *Breve,* 77.
[9] *Ibid.,* 78; Martínez, *"Diario,"* Aug. 3–4, 1863, AMCN.

High light of the stop in Ecuador was an outing on the Guayas River, where they saw many rafts made from balsa tree trunks lashed together with vines. Loaded with lumber, tropical fruit, and goods for sale, and guided by natives who took advantage of the currents and tides, these rafts often had domestic animals tethered to a shack where the family lived. Entering a branch of the river, the Spaniards found themselves in a mangrove swamp where a number of small crocodiles slept peacefully on fallen tree trunks along the green banks. Later they sampled fresh coconut milk in a palm tree forest.[10]

Indians of coastal Ecuador constructed their houses on pilings elevated to take advantage of breezes and avoid flooding. Their roofs were made of dried stalks of plants, the walls left open or partially screened with canes. Entering a typical dwelling by going up a ladder, Martínez saw one room completely open on three sides with a low wall on the side facing the river. A hammock, one old chair, a table, broken-down beds, clay water jugs, and a few dishes were the total furnishings.[11]

Back in Guayaquil the scientists met with General Juan José Flores, an Ecuadorian hero recently returned to his country from exile. Flores fought under Bolívar, proclaimed Ecuador independent, and was the first president of that country. He invited the Spaniards to a musical concert in a government building, introducing them to high society of that tropical port.[12]

Before leaving Ecuador, the naturalists prepared and boxed their scientific miscellany. Fourteen varieties of fish headed the list (corvina, chaparro, *choclizo*, and *bio* among them) followed by shellfish, mollusks, insects, reptiles, birds, plants, minerals, and rocks. On Puná Island they shot wild game, including turtledoves. They also collected items of historical and ethnological interest.[13]

Five sailing days away was Taboga Island in the Gulf of Panama about ten miles from Panama City. Reaching there on August 12, the

[10] *Ibid.*, Aug. 5, 1863, AMCN.
[11] *Ibid.*
[12] *Ibid.*
[13] *Ibid.*, Aug. 5–7, 1863, AMCN.

Spanish frigates remained in the area for a fortnight. Taboga and other offshore islands were legally a part of Panama, which in turn was a province of the republic of New Granada, later renamed Colombia. In connection with its role as terminus for the Pacific Steam Navigation Company, the island's principal buildings were quarters and a fresh-water reservoir. A large mansion on the tropical island served as a convalescent hospital for sick inhabitants of the unhealthful isthmus.[14]

Compared to other ports Taboga was a paradise: coconut palms and lush vegetation made the scenery attractive, the sea provided an abundant variety of fish as well as pearls, fresh water was plentiful, and servants of a "sweet and hospitable nature" were readily available at low cost. Inhabitants of the island dressed simply, the women in an openwork blouse and plain skirt, the men in shirt and trousers of white or colored cotton cloth. Everyone went barefoot and protected their heads from the blazing sun with finely woven straw hats from Ecuador. Martínez commented that the natives bathed frequently, splashing water over their bodies with half-gourds called *totumas*. He added, "It is a general custom to be stretched out in their hammocks most of the day."[15]

Conferring with the mayor of Taboga, the naturalists made plans to visit the pearl fisheries at Isla del Rey in the Pearl Islands not far away. The pearl divers were Negroes who, weighted down with large stones, descended about seventy to eighty feet through shark-infested water to the oyster beds. In general the oysters were sold in large lots to commercial middlemen who chose the best for themselves, then resold the remainder at a reduced price. The Spaniards found that it was possible to deal directly with the divers, giving them ten or twelve reales for a dozen oysters, most of which contained no pearls, of course.[16]

From Taboga the naturalists went to the mainland, staying at the Hotel Aspinwall in Panama City. They were shocked at the city's

[14] *Ibid.*, Aug. 7–14, 1863, AMCN.
[15] *Ibid.*, Aug. 14–15, 1863, AMCN.
[16] *Ibid.*, Aug. 15, 1863, AMCN; Almagro, *Breve*, 70.

*93*

moral and physical decay: streets were narrow and dirty, houses crumbling, stores filthy, and a great number of buildings in ruins, their walls covered by vegetation. In the plaza they saw the handsome stone cathedral "of notable architecture but uncared for externally and uncleaned on the interior; many nests of insects were in the walls."[17] Castro, the Spanish photographer, made a fine wet-plate photographic negative of the cathedral. At night the city was dark and quiet; the only lights were near the hotel. Daytime activity surged around the railroad station, where goods and passengers were transshipped on small steam vessels to and from Taboga. The railroad line crossed the isthmus to Colón, a port of call for many European and North American ships.

Searching for marine life, the Spaniards visited beaches, but the sun was so hot they could work only a short time. To avoid filling the hotel with noxious odors while preparing their specimens, they rented a native shack near the beach, giving presents to a Negro family that helped in collection and preparation. In addition to numerous crustaceans, twenty-three varieties of fish were collected, including *pámpano*, salmon, barbudo, white spider, *cocochita*, and blackeye.[18]

In mid-August, a junta presided over by Admiral Pinzón decided that the *Covadonga* should visit Pacific ports of Central America while the two frigates paid a call at San Francisco, California. Espada decided to work and live on the *Covadonga*; his four companions, Martínez, Amor, Puig, and Castro, stayed aboard the *Triunfo*. Former president Paz was on his way to Spain, and Isern and Almagro were still in Peru.

[17] Martínez, "*Diario*," Aug. 16, 1863, AMCN.
[18] *Ibid.*, Aug. 18–22, 1863, AMCN.

# X

# California and Central America

ADMIRAL PINZÓN's instructions specified that to promote good will, ships of his squadron should visit Pacific coast ports from Valparaíso, Chile, to San Francisco, California. Spain had governed the area between those cities for centuries, but the independence wars from 1810 to 1825 severed political ties to Europe and left a certain hostility in the former colonies toward their mother country. Receptions on the Spanish warships, concerts by the squadron band, banquets, and balls—all these were part of the pacification program. For the scientists accompanying the expedition, the region's fabulous wealth in the kingdoms of nature was the main attraction. When the Spanish frigates left Panama for San Francisco, the naturalists aboard looked forward to seeing placer gold diggings, grizzly bears, redwood trees, and other phenomena unique to California.

Six weeks of sailing in good weather without any stops were required for the *Triunfo's* passage from Panama to San Francisco. Both frigates left Taboga on August 27, but the flagship *Resolución* arrived earlier, even though she stopped briefly in Acapulco, Mexico, for coal. It was not convenient or wise for the Spanish squadron to make a formal visit to Mexico, because the French intervention war under way there was supported at first by Spanish troops. Life aboard the *Triunfo* was the usual routine for the naturalists—some reading, writing, chess-playing, and an occasional fish or bird to prepare. Fernando Amor's liver ailment kept him in bed. His friends took turns caring for him. At the entrance to San Francisco Bay a pilot came aboard to convey them past artillery batteries to the wharf. All ships were under close surveillance because of the Civil War in the United States.[1]

[1] Martínez, *"Diario,"* Aug. 27–Oct. 9, 1863, AMCN.

Docking in San Francisco on October 9, 1863, the Spaniards were surprised at the great size of the bay and the number of ships anchored there. Besides other foreign vessels, there were five warships of the Russian Pacific Squadron, headed by Admiral Popoff. As soon as the Spanish party landed, they put Amor in the French Hospital, where he died on October 21. He was buried in Calvary Cemetery.[2] His death and Paz's resignation reduced the scientific commission to six members, two of whom were in Peru and one in Central America. The other three spent about three weeks in northern California.

In San Francisco, a city of about 100,000 people in 1863, the naturalists registered at the Hotel California, corner of Dupont (Grant) and Commercial streets. On October 11 the Spanish Theater put on a special dramatic and musical program honoring the visitors, and five days later Spanish residents had a grand ball for them. A surviving program lists twenty-four dances: quadrille, polka, waltz, schottische, galop, *pasadoble*, habanera, and others. Other evenings were spent at the Melodian Theater and Gilbert's Theater, where on October 18 the program featured "The Adventures of Tom Tape, a tailor, and Sally Scraggs, a milliner." Martínez said that the Opera House was "magnificent," and that there were also many small theaters where Negroes entertained "with their often similar shouting and singing."[3]

Following a plan laid out for them by Edward Vischer, a Bavarian artist residing in San Francisco, Martínez and Castro took a week-long excursion to the mountainous gold-mining region of California. On October 20 a night river boat carried them to Stockton, where at daybreak the following day they caught a stagecoach to Angels Camp and Murphys. The road was so dusty that every passenger was provided with a large cotton cloak to protect his clothes during the fourteen-hour ride. After registering at the Murphys Hotel, they

---

[2] *Ibid.*, Oct. 26–28, 1863, AMCN; Benjamin Gilbert, "Welcome to the Czar's Fleet," *Calif. Hist. Soc. Quarterly*, Vol. XXVI, No. 1 (1947), 13–19.

[3] Printed theater and dance programs tipped in Martínez, *"Diario,"* Oct. 11, 16, 1863, AMCN; Almagro, *Breve*, 71.

walked around the little mining town and found a dance hall, "where some German girls were dancing with the miners for a little money." On October 22 they inspected a large placer gold mine near Murphys, where gigantic wheels lifted the water to wash the ore. A mine official presented them with a sample of gold-bearing quartz.[4]

A visit to groves of sierra redwood trees (*Sequoia gigantea*), discovered only a few years earlier, climaxed their mountain trip. The hotel prepared a lunch and furnished transportation for a visit to the Big Trees area, "one of the most delightful excursions a person could desire," said Martínez. Castro photographed some of the largest trees, while his colleague collected cones, needles, and seedlings to carry back to Spain.[5]

For their return from the mountains the Spanish naturalists rented a two-horse carriage and headed back via Campo Seco, Buckeye, and Sacramento. Martínez lamented that in California's capital, despite its name, "Spanish customs have been completely erased being substituted by American ones; now it is only remembered that this country was once a Spanish colony because of some slight accident of history." From Sacramento they took a steamship, the *Chrysopolis*, down the river to San Francisco, eight hours away. The side-wheeler was described as handsome, comfortable, and clean, with convenient services. American eating habits appalled the Europeans, who complained, "Dinner was served quickly as if those who sat down came only to satisfy their need for food; everyone ate rapidly and left the table as soon as they had finished."[6]

Before leaving California, Martínez and Ottfried Bendeleben, a Spanish-speaking German acquaintance who was employed by the artist Edward Vischer, took a trip around the southern part of San Francisco Bay. Going by carriage from Oakland, they stopped first at old Mission San José, hauntingly Iberian with its adobe walls, tile roofs and wrought-iron grilles. At the near-by spa of Warm Springs

4 Martínez, "*Diario*," Oct. 20–24, 1863, AMCN.

5 *Ibid.*, Oct. 22–23, 1863, AMCN; see also Francis P. Farquhar, "California Big Trees," *The Amer. West*, Vol. II, No. 3 (1965), 58–64.

6 Martínez, "*Diario*," Oct. 25–26, 1863, AMCN.

they lunched with the physician-proprietor before proceeding to San Jose, where they spent the night of October 28. Lunch the following day was in the mansion of the English managers of the quicksilver mine at New Almaden, named for a similar mercury deposit in Almadén, Spain. A tour of the mine followed. They descended the main shaft about 950 feet, and later saw the mills, furnaces, and workers' houses. Following an overnight stop in Santa Clara, the travelers went to Alviso, where they were able to take a bay steamship back to San Francisco.[7]

Their California visit ended on November 1, when the Spanish frigate sailed from San Francisco for Valparaíso, Chile, a nonstop cruise of seventy-four days. Admiral Pinzón's flagship, *Resolución*, left earlier, since it was scheduled to stop in Panama and Peru before returning to Chile. The only unusual entry in Martinez' daily log of the voyage described the burial of a sailor. "After lunch the crew formed on deck. The priest, in white vestments, took charge of the burial of the sailor who, in a wooden box [weighted] with stones, was thrown into the water, port side, sinking immediately."[8] When they reached Valparaíso on January 13, 1864, the naturalists went ashore, taking rooms at the same hotel at which they had stayed eight months before.

Commenting on the California visit, Almagro pointed out that the naturalists were on land for only 21 days as against 118 aboard ship. "How much more advantageous would have been the use of that time if the commission had not been subject to the movements of the naval squadron?" he asked.[9]

While the frigate carried Martínez, Amor, Castro, and Puig to California, the *Covadonga*, with zoologist Espada aboard, visited Pacific ports in Central America. For naval authorities the mission was one of good will, but Espada's primary goal was to collect items representing the natural history of Spain's former American colonies.

[7] *Ibid.*, Oct. 28–30, 1863, AMCN.
[8] *Ibid.*, Nov. 8, 1863, AMCN.
[9] Almagro, *Breve*, 72.

These specimens, sent back to Madrid, still form an important part of the displays at the Botanical Garden, Museum of Natural Science, and a number of large universities.

Leaving the Gulf of Panama on August 28, 1863, the *Covadonga* moved north to the Republic of Costa Rica. First stop was at the principal Pacific port of Puntarenas in the Gulf of Nicoya on September 3. Espada was able to examine firsthand the famed black sand beaches and obtain some fish and mollusk samples. The market was filled with coffee, tropical fruit, and goods from all over the country. It was torrid at sea level only ten degrees north of the Equator.[10]

Coasting along the shores of neighboring Nicaragua for several days, the Spanish schooner anchored on September 9 at the small port of Corinto. Espada went ashore to visit the near-by harbor of El Realejo and inland city of Chinandega. He spent two days there collecting reptiles and birds. He undoubtedly heard about the continuous political strife between the liberals of León and the conservatives of Granada, and about the Yankee filibuster, William Walker, who had recently controlled the country. But Espada was not interested in politics, nor did he remain in Nicaragua for more than a few days.[11]

The Republic of El Salvador was the last country in Central America visited by the Spanish sailing ship. Anchoring in two ports at opposite ends of the small republic, the Iberians made some investigations along the coast, then several forays inland. At Acajutla, in the north near the Guatamalan border, Espada left the ship for an excursion to the rich agricultural valley of Sonsonate. His ultimate destination was ten miles farther on, the active volcano of Izalco, near the summit of which he spent one whole day. Loaded down with mineral samples, he returned to the schooner on September 18 just as the ship was preparing to move south to the harbor of La Unión on the Gulf of Fonseca. The few days in that Salvadorian port were complicated by a local insurrection in which a Spanish belligerent had

---

[10] Unfortunately the sections of Espada's diary covering Central America are missing, but his trip is outlined in Almagro, *Breve*, 73–74.

[11] *Ibid.*, 73.

been assassinated. Supporters of the victim asked that the Spanish warship bombard the town, but the ship's captain wisely refused, saying he would refer the matter to Admiral Pinzón.[12]

On September 24, 1863, the *Covadonga* left El Salvador planning to return to Valparaíso, Chile, by way of Panama, Ecuador, and Peru. In Panama early in October Almagro joined Espada on the Spanish schooner. He stayed aboard until they reached Guayaquil, Ecuador, on October 26, then left the ship to visit Quito, capital of Ecuador and ancient Inca seat of power. Since Almagro's trip to Quito was repeated in 1864, his impressions and observations will be discussed later in connection with the second and longer visit. Meanwhile, Espada continued with the *Covadonga* to Callao, Peru, arriving there early in November to spend about a month before sailing on to Valparaíso, Chile.[13]

When he returned to Guayaquil at the end of November, 1863, Almagro decided to visit Indian ruins in northwestern Peru. He took an English ship to the Peruvian port of Huanchaco, six miles from the city of Trujillo, and in the latter city obtained preliminary information about the Chimu culture ruins while arranging for transportation and a guide to the archaeological sites. The ruins of Chan Chan, ancient capital of the Chimu Empire, lie about four miles from Trujillo and cover eleven square miles. Built mostly of sun-dried adobe bricks, the walled city once housed perhaps 250,000 people. Earthquakes, weathering, and plunderers have reduced most of the walls to rubble, but today some sections thirty feet high still remain. Because it seldom rains in that desert area, the ancient Indians constructed irrigation ditches from the Moche River and built reservoirs which enabled them to cultivate the coastal plain.

Almagro made some excavations in Chan Chan at the huacas, or burial mounds, of Concha, Obispo (renamed Esperanza), and Palacio del Sol, finding objects of clay, gold, bone, and silver. He commented on the large number of treasures that had been taken from these sites

[12] *Ibid.*; Barreiro, *Historia*, 207–208.
[13] Almagro, *Breve*, 73–74.

—others have estimated that in one twenty-year period $6,000,000 worth of gold and silver objects were removed.[14] The Chimus were particularly skilled in pottery and weaving. Their famous portrait pots reveal the sophistication of their society. Appraising the ruins of Chan Chan, Almagro wrote, "These are very far from being as grandiose as those stone ones of Cuzco and Tiahuanaco: they are earthen, and naturally time has irreparably damaged them."[15]

Returning to Huanchaco on the coast, Almagro took a steamship bound for Callao and reached the capital city on December 13, 1863. That same day Admiral Pinzón's flagship arrived in port with news that the other members of the scientific commission aboard the *Triunfo* had sailed directly to Valparaíso. Since the admiral thought he would soon be going to Chile, Almagro and Isern decided to sail with him aboard the *Resolución*, but their wait turned out to be three months long. In the meantime, they continued gathering information and specimens of Americana.[16]

Isern had not been idle during the interval when his colleagues visited Central and North American ports. His longest botanical reconnaissance was to the Chanchamayo Valley, which he visited in September and October of 1863. This river valley is located about 120 miles northeast of Lima, and although it is almost at sea level, one has to cross over the Andes Mountains to reach it.

Starting from Lima on August 31 and guided by a native, Isern followed the Rímac River to San Mateo, then on to La Oroya and over the pass descending to Tarma, which lies about 10,000 feet above sea level. From Tarma he continued on to the junction of the Tulumayo and Chanchamyo rivers, his destination being a Spaniard's hacienda in that region near the mission La Merced. Like their Inca ancestors, Isern's guides chewed coca leaves (*Erythroxylon coca*) containing alkaloids, including cocaine, which dulled their senses and

[14] Otto Holstein, "Chan-Chan: Capital of the Great Chimu," *The Geographical Rev.*, Vol. XVII (1927), 52–53.
[15] Almagro, *Breve*, 61; see also Barreiro, *Historia*, 210.
[16] Almagro, *Breve*, 61.

appetites. He later remarked that "it seems impossible that they can travel all of one day and more with [only] coca."[17]

On the route from Lima to Chanchamayo, Isern stayed at tambos, those shelters that were far from being inns or hotels. The Spanish botanist wrote that some tambos had only rum (*aguardiente de caña*), a few had bread; the best ones had those items as well as potatoes, eggs, onions, and *chalma*, or salted mutton. Natives living in these and other shacks had few necessities and fewer conveniences; "the fork and spoon of these Indians are the five fingers."[18]

In a long letter to a friend in Spain, Isern retraced his trip to Chanchamayo with many references to plants observed at different elevations. Barley and potatoes were cultivated above 10,000 feet; a thousand feet lower he saw alfalfa, wheat, and fruit trees. Farther down were willows, elders, *chugiragua*, and currant bushes. Tropical vegetation flourished in the Chanchamayo Valley: pineapples, sugar cane, bananas, cherimoyas, rice, coffee, palms, and cinchona, the source of quinine. It was so humid that rice grew without irrigation; torrential rains filled the crystalline rivers. The Spanish botanist described "forests where civilized man has not yet entered, with giant trees older than Methuselah, the vanilla plant winding itself among the trees."[19]

There were many snakes, few of them poisonous, in eastern Peru. Man's principal danger came from savage Indians like the Chunchos, "who shot their arrows at all living creatures." Because they had killed a man and wounded a woman a few days before Isern arrived, his host insisted that the botanist always travel with three armed servants. "The knife and revolver were my constant companions," he wrote his family, "in spite of which, fears and precautions robbed my sleep on more than one occasion."[20] But Isern walked hundreds of miles in Peru without being mistreated or robbed. The large herbar-

[17] Isern to Felix Borrell y Font, Lima, Peru, Nov. 29, 1863, pub. in *El Pabellón Médico*, Madrid, IV, No. 125 (Jan. 14, 1864), 26–27.
[18] *Ibid.*
[19] *Ibid.*
[20] Isern to family, Lima, Peru, Dec. 30, 1863, Barreiro, *Historia*, 209.

ium he gathered and prepared in Chanchamayo was taken to Lima, then forwarded to Madrid, where it can be seen today in the Botanical Garden.

At the end of 1863 while waiting for the frigate to depart for Chile, Isern and Almagro carried out some field investigations in the region around Lima. Describing a one-week trip to the Lurín Valley, twenty miles south of the capital, Isern recalled that he left Lima on December 21, escorted as far as the town of Lurín by two cavalry soldiers. Securing some native guides in that place, he set out the following day.

> I continued my excursions, searching more for antiquities than flowers because we were traversing sand dunes where plants are not seen. The sun was suffocating. When I dismounted, my feet burned; you could easily cook eggs on such sand. I ordered excavations to be made and we found many Indian skulls, clothing, small jewels, and a shell of great value. I spent Christmas Day in these duties. Returning [to Lima] yesterday, I arrived so parched and bedraggled, so covered with dust and perspiration that on seeing me, two officers of the frigate [*Resolución*] did not recognize me."[21]

Isern and Almagro remained in the Peruvian capital until March 8, 1864, when the *Resolución* left Callao for Valparaíso. Their stay had been prolonged when some Spanish residents requested Admiral Pinzón to protect their property, which they believed to be threatened. The tense political situation between Peru and Spain continued after the squadron moved on to Chile.

[21] *Ibid.*, 211.

# XI

# Seven Months in Chile: Caught Up in the War

THE FIRST seven months of 1864 were difficult for the Spanish scientific commission—not because of journeys through rugged terrain, but because their plans, amid a changing political situation, were necessarily uncertain. In April, when war between Spain and Peru erupted, the role of the civilian scientists became precarious. Because they were detached from the naval squadron, they had neither authorization nor funds to continue their mission. Meanwhile, waiting in Chile for new orders from the minister of public works to continue their expedition, the naturalists made some field trips to augment their knowledge and collections.

In January, Martínez stayed close to Valparaíso waiting for the rest of the group to arrive from Peru. He searched the beaches for mollusks, contracted with local fishermen to secure unusual marine life, and prepared items for shipment to Spain. During part of February and March he headquartered at the hacienda of Los Nogales near Quillota. There was a fine house on the estate surrounded by a magnificent garden of fruit trees and flowers that attracted clouds of hummingbirds. Studying and inquiring about those delicate creatures, Martínez learned that they hibernated in winter, often sleeping in hollow logs or tree holes. The owner of the hacienda, Juan Rusque, was very friendly, "as is common in this country where they welcome travelers, giving them everything necessary: horse, meal, bath, good lodging, and courteous friendliness."[1]

The hacienda had copper mines and wood-stoked kilns for smelting ore. Firewood came from the forests in oxcarts, "each time from farther away. . . . Consumption of wood is enormous since the kilns

[1] Martínez, "*Diario*," Feb. 27, Mar. 8–15, 1864, AMCN.

function day and night." Work was suspended during the rainy season, in contrast to northern Chile where the lack of rainfall permitted year-around operation. Martínez said, "It is certain that this industry is not burdened by taxes," and he noted that workers received only a small part of their pay each day, the rest at certain times of the year. This technique kept them from leaving and gave the owner more operating capital or the opportunity to earn interest on the accumulated wages. Copper miners slept outside on the ground, their food generally consisting of beans and bread.[2] What a difference between conditions of these miners and those the Spaniards observed a few months earlier in California!

Agricultural peons, the majority of the people in Chile, were not much better off. Lodged in squalid adobe huts, poorly dressed, malnourished, and uneducated, they were constantly indebted to the landowner. Keeping the pay records himself, the owner also operated a monopoly store and cantina, and he had his judge, jail, fines, and wooden pillory for delinquents. "By such means the owners are able to keep peons on the hacienda, and workers are not free to work where and how they wish, a type of slavery more hateful than that of Negroes."[3]

In the 1860's Chilean agriculture was in a depressed state. A dozen years earlier at the time of the California gold rush Chileans sold corn and wheat in great quantities at fabulous prices, but that market was later filled by growers in Oregon and California. Fruit orchards and vineyards were better off, Chilean wines being exported to most of Latin America. The visiting naturalists considered Chile's land irrigation primitive, since Chileans used open ditches, "took advantage of the accidents of nature," and had constructed no great public works to channel rivers and store or elevate water.[4]

Horsemanship was important to rural Chileans. Their greatest desire was a fine horse, elegantly harnessed. Upper-class women riders were especially skilled in riding and handling their mounts. "It

[2] *Ibid.*, Mar. 8–10, 26, 1864, AMCN.
[3] *Ibid.*, Mar. 25, 1864, AMCN.
[4] *Ibid.*, Mar. 25–29, 1864, AMCN.

is not unusual to see them on holidays," said Martínez, "wearing European hats and elegant clothing, and having more control over their horses than many men." Colorfully dressed Chilean cowboys, called *guasos*, were excellent riders like the Gauchos of Argentina or Uruguay. Each *guaso* invariably wore a poncho—a woven blanket with an opening in the center, which covered him to the upper thigh—leather boots, enormous spurs, and a wide-brimmed sombrero. His saddle was a simple wooden stool cinched over some sheepskins, the latter serving as a bedroll, while his stirrups were large and elaborate, usually made of wood and inlaid with silver decorations.[5]

In mid-March several of the Spanish naturalists saw a roundup and rodeo on a large ranch near Valparaíso. Cattle and horses were gathered into staked corrals where they were counted and branded. *Guasos* and peons demonstrated their dexterity in the spectacle of "bronco-busting." Their method was to lasso the mustang, tie it to a pole in the center of a corral, and force the animal to the ground with another rope around one leg. After saddling, bridling, and blindfolding it, the *guaso* mounted and let the horse go free, but with all the bucking and charging he had a difficult time staying on. Sometime later horse and rider returned, the former covered with sweat and bloody from the spurs. The next day the "slightly barbaric" activity was repeated.[6]

When the scientists returned to Valparaíso at the end of March, the final rupture between the civilian scientists and the naval squadron occurred. Admiral Pinzón informed Martínez that the destination of the squadron made it impossible for the scientific commission to remain aboard, and he requested them to remove all their clothing, books, collections, and equipment from the *Triunfo*. A few days later he said the naturalists would have to return to Spain by the next commercial ship. When they protested, he denied them financial assistance, even refusing to pay their accrued salaries.[7]

At an emergency meeting of the scientific commission on April 2

[5] *Ibid.*, Mar. 10, 1864, AMCN.
[6] *Ibid.*, Mar. 10, 21, 1864, AMCN.
[7] *Ibid.*, Mar. 31, Apr. 1–3, 1864, AMCN; MS 808, MN.

the group agreed to remove their effects from the frigate, but they determined not to obey the admiral's order to return home. Reasoning that the minister of public works had sent them to America, they decided that only he could recall them. Martínez was delegated to write an official letter to Madrid requesting permission and funds to carry out a scientific collecting trip across South America approximately along the second degree of south latitude.[8]

A few days later the commission received a royal communiqué dated February 20 from the minister of public works ordering them to return to Spain immediately, the order having been requested by Patricio Paz y Membiela, who was now back in the Spanish capital. Convening the group again, Martínez read the news from Spain and suggested that they ignore the order until they had an answer to their request for an extension of time. He argued that the naval squadron had been their major obstacle, but now that they were free from it, they could carry out their assignment with better results. The majority of the group agreed with their leader. On April 17 another letter was drafted and mailed to Madrid asking for governmental approval of their plan to return via the Amazon River, a trip they called the great journey (*gran viaje*).[9]

Meanwhile, hostilities erupted between Spain and Peru. Admiral Pinzón and his two frigates left Valparaíso suddenly on April 6, 1864, proceeding to the Chincha Islands off southern Peru, where the Spaniards captured a Peruvian warship and seized the three islands on April 14. This action was suggested and prompted by a hot-tempered Spanish diplomatic agent in Peru, Señor Eusebio de Salazar y Mazarredo, who felt he had been rebuffed by Peruvian officials. Rich guano fertilizer deposits on the islands, property of the Peruvian government, furnished more than three-fourths of its total income, hence their importance.[10] The course of the war between Spain and Peru, eventually joined by Chile, Bolivia, and Ecuador, will not

[8] *Ibid.*, Apr. 2–5, 1864, AMCN.
[9] *Ibid.*, Apr. 15, 1864, AMCN; similar letters sent May 17 and June 17, 1864.
[10] *Ibid.*, Apr. 6, 30, 1864, AMCN; Davis, *Last Conquistadores*, 34, 52; "*Islas Chinchas: Informe Escuadra Pacífico, 1864*," Manuscript 844, Museo Naval, Madrid.

be traced here, but its effects on the scientific commission will be discussed.

News of the seizure of the Chinchas arrived in Valparaíso the end of April, producing widespread protests against Spain and manifestations of sympathy for Peru. Newspapers editorialized against the European aggression, and public meetings and parades swelled chauvinistic patriotism. "Each day," said Martínez, "the feelings against Spain are greater. . . . Many Spaniards are thinking of seeking refuge in a foreign consulate. The newspapers are filled with insults against our country."[11]

The situation of the Spanish scientists in Chile was critical. They had been abandoned by the fleet and lacked financial resources. They were uncertain about their future course of action. Chileans identified them closely with the naval squadron and now considered them to be spies or advance agents of a Spanish plot to reconquer her former colonies. A letter Isern wrote to relatives in Spain indicates the animosity the naturalists faced:

> Inflammatory articles are inserted in the newspapers asserting that we have come to map roads and highways to prepare the conquest. I am the most compromised of the group because I have gone more by land. From time to time I go out in the country, usually with Martínez. We are armed with revolvers and daggers, determined to give our all in case we are assaulted by assassins. . . . In Santiago they want to tear down our flag flown on the house of the Spanish minister. There are many shouts of "Death to the Goths," which is what they call Spaniards here. Those of the Commission they hate still more saying that we have been sent to study the country in case of war with Spain.[12]

Martínez stayed in his hotel room many days rather than take the risk of venturing out on the street. He had planned a trip to the south of Chile but was advised to postpone it since Chileans might think he

[11] Martínez, *"Diario,"* May 3, 1864, AMCN.

[12] Isern to family, Valparaíso, Chile, May 16, 1864, in Francisco de las Barras de Aragón, *"Los últimos escritores de Indias,"* Bol. de la Real Soc. Geog., Madrid, Vol. LXXXV (1949), 69; Barreiro, *Historia,* 220.

went there to buy coal and supplies for the fleet. He seldom went out alone, but even then he heard insults shouted at him, and on one occasion a group of Chileans sang their national anthem when they saw the naturalists.[13]

In spite of unceasing hostility against Spaniards, the naturalists continued their scientific work while waiting for new orders from Spain. Packing and boxing the items removed from the frigate required a number of days, as did the paper work in securing export permits and shipping documents. The Spanish consul arranged to have the boxes forwarded to Spain, paying the cost out of his funds. Most of the Chilean scientists remained friendly with the Spaniards, giving them assistance, technical information, and specimens. From one of them Martínez bought a collection of insects, and Philippi, director of Santiago's museum, gave Isern a herbarium of 1,308 Chilean plants, all well prepared and classified. About this time Espada acquired some reptiles and two assortments of live animals, which he shipped to Spain.[14]

When heavy winter rains prevented Almagro from visiting southern Chile where the Araucanian Indians lived, he decided to visit an archaeological site near Chiuchiu, Bolivia. Leaving Valparaíso on April 17, he took a ship to the Bolivian port of Cobija (now Gatico, Chile), arriving six days later. With the help of the Spanish vice-consul in that port he secured two mules, one for cargo and one to ride, and set off across the Atacama Desert toward a destination more than one hundred miles inland. This area was completely barren, with large deposits of borax, salts, and nitrates. Hot tropical winds blew the sand, erasing the trail and molesting the traveler. "There is not any vegetation in this desert," he wrote, "and the small amount of water encountered tastes so bad that not even the animals drink it."[15]

It took six days to go from Cobija to Chiuchiu, passing through miserable stage posts named Colupo, Chacance, Guacate—each of them just an uninhabited shack. On April 26, Almagro arrived at the little town of Calama, where there was potable water; and the follow-

[13] Martínez, "Diario," May 1–5, June 1, 1864, AMCN.
[14] Ibid., June 3, 17, 22, July 5, 1864, AMCN; Almagro, Breve, 159.
[15] Ibid., 75.

ing day he entered the hamlet of Chiuchiu. Near by were the ruins of a pre-Columbian city. "Many excavations were made there," said Almagro, "and I had the pleasure of removing a number of mummies which with considerable effort were forwarded to Madrid."[16] A dozen of these now repose in the Museum of the Americas at the University of Madrid.

Almagro returned to Cobija over the same inhospitable road, the principal line of communication between towns in southern Bolivia and the coast. Mule trains used the route for carrying European merchandise from Cobija to the mountains, returning loaded with silver from the mine at Potosí. A muleteer in charge of a drove carrying 120,000 pesos in silver accompanied Almagro on the trail to Cobija.[17]

During June and July the Spanish naturalists made more field trips in Chile while they awaited further orders. Diary entries record trips to Limoche, Atocha, Cerro Castillo, Arroyo de las Zorras, several haciendas, and a Franciscan monastery. They spent some evenings in the home of the Argentine consul, Señor Becher; others with their friends Leybold, Thamm, Plagemann, Díaz, and Philippi. On July 5 they sent more boxes of scientific curiosa to Spain.[18]

Finally on July 29, 1864, Martínez received an order from the minister of public works dated June 10, 1864, authorizing their trip across South America and granting the commission 12,000 pesetas for their expenses. Since their plans called for initiating the cross-continental campaign at Guayaquil, Ecuador, it was decided to move the headquarters there while making preparations for the trip. Espada and Isern remained in Chile for two months, but Martínez, Almagro, and Castro sailed to Guayaquil on the August packet ship.[19]

The trip to Ecuador was tiring because it lasted three weeks and trying because the Spanish passengers had to pass along the full length of the Peruvian coast. After the seizure of the Chincha Islands the naturalists were not permitted to go ashore in most Peruvian ports,

[16] *Ibid.*
[17] *Ibid.*, 76.
[18] Martínez, *"Diario,"* June 3, July 10–13, 1864, AMCN.
[19] *Ibid.*, July 29, Aug. 11, 1864, AMCN; Barreiro, *Historia*, 226, 397.

Map showing South American phase of the expedition

and aboard ship they endured "insults to their persons and vulgarities against Spain." As they passed the Chinchas, they saw the three ships of the Spanish squadron anchored there. The coastal steamer discharged and received cargo at thirty ports, some of which were too shallow to enter, so that the merchandise had to be lightened on small craft. At Cobija they used "monkey boats," which were rafts floating on inflated sea-cow skins; at Huanchaco the native rafts known as *caballitos* (little horses) were supported by two bundles of totoras reeds about twenty feet long; at San José de Lambayeque rafts with sails transferred goods from ship to shore. When the coastal steamer anchored at Guayaquil on the last day of August, the Spaniards went ashore and lodged at the Hotel de France.[20]

Back in Valparaíso, zoologist Espada was trying to assemble a collection of live South American animals for Madrid's Zoological Garden. One can imagine his problems in having suitable cages built, transferring the animals, arranging care and feeding, and obtaining the necessary shipping documents. Early in October the menagerie of eighty-six mammals and birds was on the dock ready to go. The shipment included condors, turtledoves, partridges, swans, and male and female guanaco, bear, coypu, chinchilla, Patagonian hare, and mountain sheep. An old Spanish farm laborer who wished to return home was put in charge of the live cargo.[21]

The story of the animal shipment could be called a "zoo tragedy." The French frigate *Persévérance* carried the crated animals from Valparaíso to Le Havre, a three-month voyage during which half of the animals died and the remainder arrived in poor condition. The Spanish consul in Le Havre, having received no instructions, wrote to Madrid advising officials of the arrival of the animals and requested forwarding advice. He remarked that the old man caring for the animals "completely lacks initiative and the conditions for carrying out his task." From France to Spain the animals traveled by railroad, but at the border the rail car got sidetracked for several days. Upon

[20] Martínez, *"Diario,"* Aug. 11–31, 1864, AMCN. Similar native barges described in Tom B. Jones, *South America Rediscovered*, 154, 157.

[21] Folio 2, *legajo* 1865, Paz Graells Corresp., AMCN.

arrival in Madrid in January, 1865, the starving and freezing animals were detained by customs officials, and when finally delivered to the zoo, there were only twenty-three left of the original eighty-six. The following year Almagro reported that only ten of the animals shipped from Chile were still alive.[22]

When they finished their projects in Chile early in October, 1864, Espada and Isern made plans to join their colleagues in Ecuador. Isern had dispatched thirty boxes of dried Chilean plants to Madrid. Unlike the animals, they arrived in good condition. The trip north to Guayaquil was almost identical to that of Martínez except that Isern and Espada had difficulty with their luggage. In two Peruvian ports officials were suspicious of their forty-eight pieces of baggage and opened one or two to find only stuffed partridges. Espada learned that the trouble stemmed from the bill of lading, which listed the boxes and stated "with munitions." This referred to the shotguns and ammunition carried by the naturalists for their use in the field. On the last day of October they reached Guayaquil.[23]

Bartolomé Puig, the taxidermist, and Rafael Castro, photographer for the commission, quit the expedition at this time. Puig said he could not continue working with the scientific commission because of chronic hepatitis. But his colleagues knew that it was his heart, not his liver, that was affected, for on July 28, 1864, he had married Señorita Nieves Martínez, daughter of a rich Spanish landowner residing in Chile. A few years later Puig and his wife went back to Spain. Because Castro did not want to undertake the arduous crossing of South America by mule and canoe, he returned to Spain by commercial ship. Records in Madrid's Museum of Natural Science indicate that he died in 1865 soon after arriving home.[24] The exodus of the two auxiliary members left Martínez, Almagro, Isern, and Espada in Ecuador ready to begin their *gran viaje* across South America.

[22] Folio 24 E, *legajo* 1865, Paz Graells Corresp., AMCN; Almagro *Breve*, n. 171.

[23] Jiménez de la Espada, *Diario*, 108, 111.

[24] *Legajo* 1868, *Cartas re instancia de José Mudarra, fotógrafo*, Paz Graells Corresp., AMCN; Barreiro, *Historia*, 226–27.

# XII

# Guayaquil to Quito: The Gran Viaje

I NSTEAD OF returning to Spain by comfortable steamship as ordered by Admiral Pinzón, the remaining four naturalists of the scientific commission decided to cross South America at its widest part, from Guayaquil, Ecuador, to Belém, Brazil. Their plan involved crossing the Andes Mountains again, descending the Napo and Amazon rivers in native dugouts, and enduring the inconvenience and suffering of travel by mule and canoe through rugged territory with unsalubrious climates, all the while plagued by unsanitary water, insects, and snakes. Why should such an adventure be launched by men who had already experienced two years of privations in America? It appears they were not satisfied with their accomplishments and wanted to embellish their collections by penetrating the fertile heart land of South America. Almagro stated it succinctly: "We wanted to carry out a truly scientific trip, leaving aside all our comforts and exposing ourselves to a thousand more or less dangerous vicissitudes, which would redound to our detriment and benefit science."[1]

Although the scientists were now liberated from the rigid schedule and discipline to which they were subject while attached to the naval squadron, they had only exchanged one set of problems for another. Instead of suffering from seasickness and ship movement, they would be saddle weary and footsore; rather than quarrels with recalcitrant sailors or martinet officers, they now had to put up with the "insensibility and inertia" of their Indian guides and porters; no longer cooped up in a small stateroom, they were confined to a grass shack or a portable tent; and they still had to travel within limited time, meeting a schedule agreed upon with their leader, Martínez.

[1] Almagro, *Breve*, 74.

Guayaquil, point of departure for the long way home, was a busy city. As Ecuador's only port with connections to the capital and interior cities, it was a funnel for commerce. Virtually all foreign articles imported to the republic entered there, and the export items of cacao, lumber, tobacco, coffee, sugar, brandy, and rubber left Ecuador through Guayaquil. Founded in the sixteenth century, the city had a history marked by catastrophes: several times it was destroyed by fire, sacked by pirates, despoiled by revolution, and decimated by epidemics. In 1864, Guayaquil's population was about twenty thousand and most of its buildings were made of wood.[2]

Martínez, Almagro, and Castro explored the region around Guayaquil for items to add to their collections. On September 5 they boarded a balsa raft for a trip up the salty Guayas River, riding with the tides and tying up to a tree while the flow reversed. A cloud of mosquitoes constantly molested them and kept them from sleeping even under mosquito nets. Crocodiles occasionally swam near the raft, and others sunned themselves on the banks. The naturalists, frequently stopping to gather plants, birds, insects, and mollusks along the shore, arrived at the junction of the Pimocha River four days later and continued up that stream in a dugout canoe to the village of Bodegas.[3]

At Bodegas their hotel was a large raft divided into compartments; there was no roof or ceiling, only floor and woven-mat walls. Excerpts from Martínez' diary reveal something about life in Bodegas:

> I never thought I would encounter such a dirty and poverty-stricken place along the route to the interior. It is a pity that such beautiful landscapes and vegetation are spoiled by the town. Thatch-roofed shacks are on wooden pilings. A large number of Indian men walk in the street with their oars; they work taking cargoes to the villages along the river. They wear only a felt hat, a white poncho, and short pants; legs and feet are bare. Indians all have canoes with which they look for things to feed their families, hunting, gathering, or trading cultivated products in the markets: cacao, tobacco, coffee,

[2] *Ibid.*, 78.
[3] Martínez, *"Diario,"* Sept. 5–9, 1864, AMCN.

rice, sugarcane, coconuts, mangos, *guanabanas,* pineapple, avocados, watermelon, bananas, *mamey, pomarrosas,* oranges.[4]

After their return to Pimocha, while waiting for the river boat which would take them back to Guayaquil, the Spaniards watched natives capture crocodiles. Two Indians held a long pole in the water with a leather strap lasso at the end while a third man had a duck on a long rope. The bird was forced to fly low near the river bank, and the crocodile was lassoed while trying to catch the duck. When the reptile was tired of trying to escape his noose, he was dragged to the shore and hit on the head until dead. At that point the animal emitted a strong musky odor. The run down river on the steamship *Washington* took only eight hours, and Martínez said they had a good dinner aboard.[5]

During the last two weeks of September the naturalists visited the hacienda of Dr. Alcides Destruge. First they went by boat to Daule, a town on the river of the same name, "much more picturesque than the Guayas River and a richer valley due to plantations, especially tobacco." They spent all day there looking for horses to hire, but because of a local revolt in which riding animals had been commandeered, mounts were scarce. About sundown the mayor gave them his, and they set off, crossing the river in a canoe while the horses swam. Martínez said, "As usual the guide lost his way," so they stumbled in the dark through banana and cacao plantations, being thrown from their horses at least once. Finally they arrived at the hacienda, an oasis in the tropics.[6]

Soon after arriving at the rural estate, Almagro and Martínez went out to hunt insects by lamplight and on following days shot birds, trapped toads and iguanas, and gathered plants of the area. Near Chonana they visited an Indian burial site where Almagro extracted some human bones and artifacts. Dr. Destruge gave the visitors his personal collection of mounted reptiles. At the hacienda

[4] *Ibid.,* Sept. 9–11, 1864, AMCN; Manuel Villavicencio, *Geografía de la república del Ecuador.*

[5] Martínez, *"Diario,"* Sept. 11–12, 1864, AMCN.

[6] *Ibid.,* Sept. 17–19, 1864, AMCN.

one Spaniard remarked, "Mosquitoes were the only thing that de-
tracted from the tranquility in which we remained in this house in the
company of an educated and charming man surrounded by a com-
mendable family."[7] On the way back to Guayaquil they visited a
primitive sugar mill and stayed overnight on a raft hotel, plagued
again by mosquitoes.

Boxing the accumulated scientific items for shipment to Spain kept
Martínez occupied during the first week of October. He also arranged for Castro's return home and made preparations for the four
naturalists' journey to Quito and beyond. Leaving Almagro some
money and instructions to wait for Espada and Isern, Martínez left
Guayaquil on October 8 and headed for Ecuador's capital. The
others would follow a few weeks later.[8]

Although Quito is only 170 miles northeast of Guayaquil, it took
Martínez ten days to cover the distance by the most direct route. Not
only was it a matter of going from sea level to over nine thousand feet
altitude, rising well above that on the way, but "the roads were in-
fernal—rocks, mud, fallen trees, rivers to ford, vines and vegetation
to cut, frequent torrential rains."[9] The first section of the trip was by
steamboat to Babahoyo, also called La Bodega, a ten-hour ride to the
confluence of the Guayas and Caracol rivers. The hotel in that place
provided only a key and a bare room, no bed, bedding, or any furniture, but Martínez had his bedroll and camping equipment.

Securing a horse, mule, and native guide in Babahoyo, Martínez
set off along the road to the interior. The first night he slept at the
hacienda of Columa, the next night at Guaranda, "a pitiful village."
Indians wearing red wool ponchos and hats covered with rubber,
their trousers made of leather "from dogs or cattle," warned that
rugged terrain lay ahead. On September 13 he passed near the
famous volcano, Chimborazo, which rises over twenty thousand feet
into the air, but clouds and fog kept him from seeing the top of the
mountain. He did see the snow on its sides, and he felt the wind

[7] *Ibid.*, Sept. 19–27, 1864, AMCN.
[8] *Ibid.*, Oct. 3–8, 1864, AMCN.
[9] *Ibid.*, Oct. 10, 1864, AMCN.

blowing from that direction. The temperature was twelve degrees centigrade. That night he stayed in a tambo called Chuguipoyo, from which he could see the volcano Cotopaxi, almost as high as Chimborazo. "As generally happens in these tambos there was nothing more than a platform on which the traveler puts his bedroll; sometimes it is made of leather. The legion of fleas was inescapable and they molested us," wrote Martínez.[10]

Martínez continued on toward Ambato, having difficulty finding the road but enjoying the spectacular mountain scenery. In his notebook he sketched the majestic volcanoes as they appeared from the trail. Indians of that area used llamas and donkeys as beasts of burden, but burros and mules were replacing the "camels of the Andes" because the native animals could carry only a quintal, about one hundred pounds. Some women he met on the road begged him to sell them cloth, believing he was a merchant. From another group he bought strawberries and gave them to the guide to put with their food. (Later that day Martínez discovered that the guide had eaten all the berries.) In late afternoon of September 14 he reached Ambato, located in a river valley of the same name. Because of its wide streets, clean houses, orchards and gardens, and near-by mountains, Martínez called it "one of the prettiest towns in Ecuador."[11]

The journey from Ambato to Quito took three days, the first stop being Pillaso, where he lodged in the house of the local military commander. Martínez found himself in the midst of a fair and fiesta in celebration of the town's saint's day. There was not much sleep that night. Nevertheless, he left at six the next morning, passed through Tacunga about noon, and stayed that night at a ranch house close to the volcano Cotopaxi, the world's highest active volcano. He could feel the strong detonations, hear the explosions, and see plume-shaped smoke puffs at the volcano's peak. On October 17, Martínez visited the ruins of an Inca palace at the hacienda of Pachusala. His description leaves no doubt that Inca artisans designed and executed these buildings:

[10] *Ibid.*, Oct. 8–14, 1864, AMCN.
[11] *Ibid.*, Oct. 14, 1864, AMCN.

There were some walls constructed from dark gray lava blocks shaped like parallelograms. The faces of the blocks are somewhat convex, and the stones are linked to one another in such a manner that it results in a solid mass. The doorways of the rooms are not symmetrical being wider at the bottom. Because of these techniques they have survived earthquakes that have ruined all the land around the volcano.[12]

After a stop at the tambo of Romesillo, where he gave his bed to "a sick priest who was said to be Spanish and who had been expelled from New Granada," Martínez arrived in Quito on October 18 and stayed at a new hotel facing St. Augustine Plaza.[13]

Almagro, Espada, and Isern took twice as long to reach Quito from the coast because they took a more circuitous route and stopped to climb two volcanoes. They also were burdened with most of the commission's equipment, which required a pack train of fifty mules. During the trip, stops were necessary to rearrange falling cargo, and at night camping spots had to be chosen near pasture, or else the men were obliged to cut grass for the animals. The Indian guides, servants, and muleteers were less trouble than the mules, for they could subsist on bananas and the food in their packs. Two of the helpers, Pancho and Juan, had accompanied Espada from Chile and stayed with the group until they reached Pernambuco, Brazil. Three dogs completed the roster of the Spanish equatorial safari.[14]

Leaving Guayaquil in mid-November, the party of naturalists headed inland by way of Babahoyo. They slept near the village of Mona on the seventeenth and in Zeiba along the Pisagua River the following night. For supper they cooked two chickens with some yuca and also had a few hard-boiled eggs. Other nights they had rice and pork or chicken and rice stew. The forests and plantations near Zeiba were delightful, and the Spaniards used their shotguns and nets to bag birds, butterflies, bats, insects, and a few ground animals.

[12] *Ibid.*, Oct. 17, 1864, AMCN.
[13] *Ibid.*, Oct. 17–18, 1864, AMCN.
[14] Almagro, *Breve*, 79; Jiménez de la Espada, *Diario*, 122–23.

Oranges, bananas, and sugar cane were cultivated by the natives, who lived in houses made from cane with thatched roofs of palm fronds.[15]

Near the village of Jorge they came upon a fiesta, "which without interruption lasted a month and was a gathering of men and women who, with the pretext of celebrating a saint's day (in this case it was the Virgin and called fiesta de Angas), do nothing except drink brandy and *guarapo*, fermented sugar-cane juice." The Indians danced to European and Ecuadorian music played by four musicians with a drum, fiddle, clarinet, and cornet. Repeatedly invited to drink the *guarapo*, Espada tried it and said it was dirty yellow in color and had a bittersweet taste similar to cider with an aftertaste of molasses. He gave one of the women a small knife for trimming fingernails, but said she would probably use it "to bleed animals and even Christians."[16]

Continuing on the zigzag trail that gradually led to higher elevations, the Spaniards noticed that the vegetation and scenery changed as the climate got colder. In the village of Chima, Espada commented on an old house in which they stayed. "They gave me a pigsty for a room, and I slept on the horse blanket and saddle. In the kitchen there were five dogs, three cats, various litters, and a crying child. I saw, or almost saw because they did it without light, preparation of the *locro* (potatoes and a mangled chicken); nevertheless, I hungrily ate that stew."[17] At Guaranda the travelers stayed five days, resting and surveying the area near by.

On November 26, Isern and Espada, with two servants, a guide, four mules, and five horses, left Almagro and the pack train for an attempt to ascend Chimborazo, the highest peak in Ecuador. Earlier in the century Baron Alexander von Humboldt had gone most of the way up the majestic peak, as had the French naturalist Jean Baptiste Boussingault. Espada went ahead of Isern, but he had to turn back on the second afternoon because of a snowstorm. A letter from Isern gives some details of their experiences on the climb:

[15] *Ibid.*, 123–25.
[16] *Ibid.*, 126–27.
[17] *Ibid.*, 128–29.

The 27th Espada and I climbed the great Chimborazo. I arrived at the rim of the perpetual snowfall but could go no farther because I was breathing with difficulty and had begun to spit blood. I watched Espada and his companion until I could see them no longer. Descending slowly, I gathered the few plants growing close to the snow. The most abundant of the vegetation was a lichen which grew in the cracks. A little farther down I found pretty composites with their petals inclined and covered with a thick fuzz which protected them from the very cold and elevated region. What moments of pleasure so difficult to describe but so easy to remember! . . . It became three, four, then five in the afternoon and Espada had not returned. Towards nightfall I feared a disaster, and not being able to give assistance I descended intending to stop at the first Indian hut which I came across. At eight I arrived at a hut of a family of Indians; thanks to my guide who spoke Quechua we were able to arrange for the head of the house to accompany me the next day in the search for my companion. Fortunately we found Espada shortly after starting the search.[18]

Reunited, the two Spaniards and their companions rode on toward Ambato, where they arrived on November 29.

Three days later, accompanied by Pancho and a guide, Espada set off to climb Cotopaxi, "which resembled a gigantic marble altar in which a sacrifice was being consumed as if in raising a tribute from earth to sky." They made camp that night in the midst of a thick mist which covered everything completely. Later it began to snow; then Espada's horse broke his tether rope, and Pancho and the guide ran after him, not returning until the following morning. Moving carefully through the snow, Espada visited a recent lava flow called Alurcurco and noticed the strong odor of sulphur emitted by the volcano. Since the men and horses suffered from *soroche* (altitude sickness), they abandoned the attempt to reach the top and descended to the town of Mulaló, where Espada stayed with the village priest in his humble quarters.[19]

18 Isern to Mariano Paz Graells, Quito, Ecuador, Jan. 3, 1865, Barreiro, *Historia*, 249–50, 271–72, 278; hereafter cited as Isern letter VI.
19 Jiménez de la Espada, *Diario*, 140–42.

Two more days of travel brought Espada and Isern to Quito on December 6; Almagro arrived four days later, since he had detoured via Riobamba. Their overland trek of three weeks had been exhausting, but they felt it was well worth it. Almagro was particularly struck by Ecuador's natural beauty:

> The dangerous, inconvenient, and inhospitable road from Babahoyo to Quito is only comparable to the beauty and majesty of the sites that we passed; Chimborazo's mass of ice, the explosions and flames of Sangay, the torrents of black smoke that haughty Cotopaxi emits are marvels of nature. . . . Whatever fatigue, whatever inconvenience of such an arduous trip is generously compensated by the magnificent panoramas enjoyed all along the road . . . above all from the plain named Cayo [Callo] at the foot of Cotopaxi.[20]

Temporary headquarters for the scientific commission in Quito was the Hotel Americana, where one sign proclaimed that it was off limits to those wearing ponchos and another warned that female guests after six in the evening could enter only with the approval of the owner.[21] Reunited with Martínez, the Spanish scientists spent more than two months in and around Ecuador's capital.

[20] Almagro, *Breve*, 80; Martínez, *"Diario,"* Dec. 6, 10, 1864, AMCN.
[21] Jiménez de la Espada, *Diario*, 143.

# XIII

# In the Land of the Quitu Indians

T HE FOUR Spanish naturalists found the region around Quito, Ecuador, a rich place for scientific exploration and an excellent base camp for their projected trip down the Napo and Amazon rivers. Located almost on the Equator at an elevation of 9,300 feet, Quito was built at the base of the Volcano Pichincha, which erupted in 1660 destroying the city. Rebuilt in the same place, it had a population in 1864 of about 50,000, the majority of whom were pure Indians, with a few residents of Spanish blood and even fewer mestizos, people of mixed race. Although there was no theater or museum in the capital, there was a university that had been established in 1787. The visiting Spaniards were surprised to find only one horse carriage in the city. It had been brought there in pieces by mule train from Guayaquil along the same route they had followed.[1]

Almagro tried to learn something of the history of Ecuador. The sketch that follows is taken from his account.

Quito was a pre-Columbian city, capital of the empire of the Quitu Indians, governed by *shiris*, whose badge of office was a large emerald worn on the forehead. Quechua-speaking Incas invaded the territory, and after the Battle of Hatuntaqui in 1470, supplanted their rule and language. The Inca conqueror Huayna Capac united with a Quitu princess. Their son was the last Inca emperor, Atahualpa. Spanish forces under Sebastián de Belalcázar captured Quito in 1533, and it remained a Spanish administrative center for almost three hundred years. The city's monumental buildings—government palace, cathedral, churches, and convents—date from the colonial period. Ecuador achieved its independence from Spain after the Battle of

[1] Almagro, *Breve*, 83–84.

Pichincha in 1822. In subsequent decades numerous rebellions and wars drained the treasury, depleted manpower, and abetted the horrible poverty all over the republic. Almagro said, "It is the most wretched of all the Latin American republics, and its total income is derived from collections at the customhouse in Guayaquil."[2]

Spain's diplomatic representative to Ecuador, Mariano del Prado, and his secretary, Conde de la Vega, aided the naturalists in many ways during their months in Quito. From diary entries of the visitors it is clear that they spent most of their evenings in Quito at the home of the minister, and the secretary accompanied them on some of their forays outside the town. He also helped them prepare their boxes for shipment to Spain. Señor del Prado presented the scientists to President Gabriel García Moreno, Vice-President Carvajal, and other officials of Ecuador. Martínez said that the president, a professional journalist, had a good collection of native minerals, and having climbed the major mountains of his country, he gave the visitors advice about techniques and equipment to use in scaling the Andes. Politically a conservative, García Moreno had recently signed a concordat with the Vatican, and he kept his country from joining Peru and Chile in the war against Spain.[3]

Dr. Manuel Villavicencio, an Ecuadorian physician and geographer, was a key acquaintance of the four Spaniards. Formerly a governor of the province of Napo, he had carried out many expeditions in central and eastern Ecuador. His reports, maps, and published geography of Ecuador were of great use to the naturalists. When Patricio Paz, former president of the scientific commission, was in Ecuador on his return to Spain, he commissioned Villavicencio to prepare an assortment of native animals. A year later Martínez took possession of the extensive collection, most of which had been purchased from hunters and taxidermists.[4]

An English botanist, William Jameson, who resided in Quito and

---

[2] *Ibid.*, 82; *see also* 81, 83.

[3] Martínez, *"Diario,"* Oct. 25–26, Nov. 23, 1864, Feb. 4, 1865, AMCN. Ecuador declared war on Spain on Feb. 27, 1866.

[4] *Ibid.*, Oct. 24, 1864, AMCN.

taught at the university there, showed the visiting Spaniards his collections and gave them a select herbarium. Most interesting among these plants were those that grow above thirteen thousand feet altitude: *Ranunculus peruvianus, Helenium asclepiadea, Valeriana microphylla*. In his spare time he collected and prepared hummingbirds (*quindis,* as they were called in Ecuador) for European museums. Advice and suggestions from Jameson and Villavicencio, as well as the use of their laboratories and libraries, contributed substantially to the success of the visit to Ecuador.[5]

Martínez spent four months in the area around Quito. Much of his time was occupied by excursions to volcanoes and collecting expeditions in the countryside. Otavalo, a picturesque town about forty-five miles northeast of the capital, was the destination when, accompanied by a hunter-guide named Chamorro, he took a horseback trip in late October and early November. Passing through the village of Guallabamba, "which travelers avoid when possible, fleeing from the fevers easily acquired there," they stayed at the adobe tambo of San Rafael. Next day they caught insects and hummingbirds in the Pisque River valley and spent the afternoon and night in Tabacundo. Martínez stayed in a private home in Otavalo and visited several of the weaving establishments, where he saw natives producing cotton and woolen cloth, ponchos, and rugs. On the first of November he went bird hunting with some clerics who used the *bodoquera,* native blowgun that launches hardened clay pellets. One of the advantages of this weapon was that "the animal remained without blood and in perfect condition for stuffing." Rabbits, deer, ducks, fish, and *cuy,* or *cobayo,* that important South American rodent, were also bagged and tagged by the hunting party.[6]

The poverty of the country and the difficulty of working with Indians impressed Martínez. He thought the land was rich and could be extremely productive "if its people were numerous and good workers." Indian tradesmen were so poor that they lacked simple supplies for carrying on their trade. When one took shoes to a shoe-

[5] *Ibid.,* Nov. 11, 1864, AMCN; Barreiro, *Historia,* 273.
[6] Martínez, "*Diario,*" Oct. 29–Nov. 2, 1864, AMCN.

maker for repair, one had to furnish the patching leather or advance him the money to buy it. "The washerwomen demand money for soap when you give them clothes to wash." One custom that demoralized foreigners was that Indians would do only what they felt like doing. For example, Martínez' guide, although he had been paid for a longer trip, suddenly decided he wanted to return to Quito; and the naturalist had to change his plans to suit those of his servant. Because of revolutions and forced labor practices, rural Ecuadorians were not very friendly with strangers, especially those who appeared to come from the city. The guide was careful to tell the people that Martínez was a foreign visitor and not a military or government official.[7]

Haciendas in the highland of Ecuador were centers of misery, where "one is surprised at the poverty which reigns there—even in ideas." Visiting one of these plantations near Quito, Martínez had the opportunity to talk with the Indian workers and Caucasian owners. His observations match those of the other members of the scientific commission, but are somewhat sharper:

> What a difference between these haciendas and those of Chile! [Here there is] disorder, filth, no conveniences, a monastic appearance, poor food badly served, ragged Indians for peons, Negresses cooking on the ground in some broken pots. Along with this the miserable chapel, old and poor furniture, plainness of the owner's clothes, and disorder in cultivation. . . . Destined to produce what they consume with no export of their surplus and having peons who owe more than they can pay in their lifetime results in a kind of slavery which is not even compensated by good and abundant food. Owners cannot be bothered with feeding the peons; they live on what they save rather than what they produce. If this were tempered by prudent humility it could be tolerated, but rare is the landowner who does not make references to indicate that he is noble, a descendant of whites, and who does not abuse the idea of manual labor, it being impossible for him. He also refers to the Indians as ignorant.[8]

[7] *Ibid.*, Nov. 4, 1864, AMCN.
[8] *Ibid.*, Nov. 5, 1864, AMCN.

In spite of their shortcomings the haciendas of Ecuador usually provided hospitality for travelers, a necessity in a country that lacked rural roads and inns.

On an excursion in the middle of November, Martínez visited the area near Cayambe Peak. A fiesta was in progress in the town of Cayambe, "beginning like all the rest with a religious service and ending with a dance where all the Indians get drunk." Music was provided by a drum and cane flute; the native dancers formed a circle one behind the other or occasionally side by side in a double circle. The men all wore short cotton trousers, woolen ponchos, and felt hats coated with rubber to protect them from the heavy rains; and the women dressed in short skirts of brilliant colors. Martínez' guide disappeared, but he continued on alone over difficult trails full of rocks and mud, fording rivers, crossing mountains, and asking for information at huts along the way.[9]

Near Cangagua, Martínez examined the ruins of an ancient Indian *pucará*, or fortress, built by placing rock walls in concentric circles around a hill. A large rock served as a signal bell; when he struck it with another stone, the sound carried well. Not far away was Puntiachil, an Indian burial place built of adobe blocks in the form of a rectangular truncated pyramid. The base was 190 feet long and 92 feet wide, the top measured 85 by 20 feet, and the platform was about 16 feet high. Mummified remains and artifacts of Cayambe and Tola Indians were found at the site. Continuing on to the hacienda of Pambamarca, the Spanish naturalist saw the house where the French academicians Bouguer and La Condamine stayed more than a century earlier on their expedition to measure a meridional arc at the Equator. After a week in the field Martínez returned to Quito with a fine collection of birds, insects, and plants, and his journal filled with notes and drawings made on the trip.[10]

The climbing of Pichincha Volcano was probably the most memorable side trip for the Spaniards during their stay in Ecuador. On December 9 a party composed of Martínez, Espada and his two ser-

[9] *Ibid.*, Nov. 12, 1864, AMCN.
[10] *Ibid.*, Nov. 15–19, 1864, AMCN.

vants, Isern, the legation secretary, and a guide left Quito. They were joined the next day by Almagro and his servant Joaquín. They spent the first night at Palmira hacienda—"poor in buildings but rich in vistas," according to Martínez—and the second night in a shepherd's shack. The third day, after walking through woods and tall grass and then over fractured volcanic rocks, they reached the edge of the crater and wanted to descend to explore it. But the guide did not know the trail and refused to go down, probably because of local superstitions about a devil who lived there. The view was spectacular, for they could see the snow-covered peaks of Cayambe, Antisana, Cotopaxi, Iliniza, Chimborazo, and a spiral of smoke from Sangay—all of these over seventeen thousand feet high. After gathering some plants and rare birds, the explorers returned to a shelter part way down the mountain.[11]

Very early on December 12, with a new guide, the naturalists tried to descend into Pichincha's crater, in spite of threatening weather and a recent snowfall. The guide, Martínez, and the others soon turned back, but Espada continued on alone, chopping steps with an ice axe. When he did not return to the top by late afternoon, his companions went back to the shack, leaving the guide at the top of the crater. For the next three days rescue parties searched for Espada, while others notified authorities and went to a near-by ranch for food and more Indian guides. Finally, on December 16, Espada met a search party and walked back to the shelter with them. While lost in the immense crater he had slept under a large rock ledge. For food he had only the loaf of bread and a quarter of a chicken in his knapsack. It snowed, rained, and there were earthquakes, but during those four days Espada explored the geological formations, gathering evidence to prove that there was stability and life in the basin, contrary to the published opinions of La Condamine and Humboldt. His notes, written under those trying circumstances, do not show that he was worried about his chances for survival or about what his companions would think or do. Perhaps even stranger was his desire to return to

[11] *Ibid.*, Dec. 9–11, 1864, AMCN; Jiménez de la Espada, *Diario*, 143–44.

the crater alone, which he did six weeks later, that time without getting lost.[12]

The harvest of specimens from Pichincha was considerable, especially of plants. Isern wrote:

> I made a fine collection of pretty and rare species to the number of one hundred sixty some. What vegetation so similar to that of our mountains! The ranunculus, barberries, violets, mosses, lichens, mushrooms . . . are representative of the European types. . . . The composites are of distinct genera . . . one of the species grows close to the top of the great Pichincha. Plants that survive at this altitude do not bear fruit, I suppose because they lack the necessary warmth.[13]

Espada's collection from the crater included mushrooms, lichen, a bird's nest and eggs, pumice, and sulphur.[14]

Antisana Volcano, southeast of Quito, was the only other major mountain the Spanish naturalists climbed. Isern was ill and remained behind, but the others, accompanied by their servants and a guide, took a twelve-day excursion to Antisana. Leaving Quito on December 28, they rode all day in the rain, fording rivers where the water came halfway up a horse's body. By nightfall they were drenched, their equipment was soaked, and they could not find a place to stay. At Valencia hacienda, after first being denied food, they were given some potatoes and cheese and permission to sleep in the sheep shed. Two more days of travel over difficult trails brought them to the tambo of Antisana at thirteen thousand feet altitude, where they stayed in one room with the keeper and his family. The only light in the shelter came from a single window one foot square, and the Indian family who lived there spoke no Spanish. Espada was amazed that humans could live at such a high altitude, braving the rugged climate and bleak, rocky terrain.[15]

[12] Martínez, *"Diario,"* Dec. 12–16, 1864, AMCN; Jiménez de la Espada, *Diario,* 144–46, 155.

[13] Isern letter VI.

[14] Jiménez de la Espada, *Diario,* 271–72.

[15] Martínez, *"Diario,"* Dec. 28–30, 1864, AMCN; Jiménez de la Espada, *Diario,* 146–47.

The Spanish scientists spent the first five days of 1865 studying the geology and ecology of Antisana. Espada examined the crater, Martínez gathered plants and insects, and Almagro tried to learn some of the legends and history of the volcano. Indian tradition held that the last eruption "was not fire but lava and rocks accompanied by tremendous noise that came from the volcano." Following this explosion the crater sank to its present level, according to local informants. Before leaving the slopes of Antisana, the visitors examined the many hot springs, lakes, and rivers, filling pages of their journals with temperature and barometric readings. When they returned to Quito on January 8, they brought back a deer, a fox, ducks, birds, parasites, plants, and mineral specimens.[16]

Preparations for their trip to the Amazon Basin required more than two months. All their baggage, equipment, and collections had to be repacked in bundles not exceeding fifty pounds each, since they would be carried on the backs of Indians for at least two weeks. Estimating that two hundred carriers would be required and advised that such a number could not be assembled at one time, Martínez decided to split the cargo, sending it as porters became available. From time to time Indians from the jungle to the east appeared in Quito, and through intermediaries they were hired for the Spanish commission. Eventually Martínez engaged Antonio Carvajal, who agreed to accompany the Spaniards to Tabatinga at the junction of the Napo and Amazon rivers on the border of Peru and Brazil. Carvajal was to serve as chief guide, recruiter of Indian bearers, and general overseer of the expedition.[17]

Payment for porters and those who would supply food, canoes, and other assistance during the expedition was generally made in trade goods. Almagro and Martínez purchased knives, machetes, mirrors, crosses, metal medallions, glass beads, flutes, spoons, ribbons, needles, thread, scissors, and almost two thousand yards of *tocuyo*, a coarse cotton cloth woven in Ecuador and highly valued by the In-

---

[16] Martínez, *"Diario,"* Jan. 1–8, 1865, AMCN; Jiménez de la Espada, *Diario*, 147–54.

[17] Martínez, *"Diario,"* Dec. 18–22, 1864, AMCN.

Broderick firehouse, San Francisco, California, October, 1863.

Russian Hill, San Francisco, as it appeared in October, 1863.

A view of Powell Street near Market Street, San Francisco, October, 1863.

Redwood trees in Calaveras County, California, October, 1863.

A placer gold mine at Murphys, California, October, 1863.

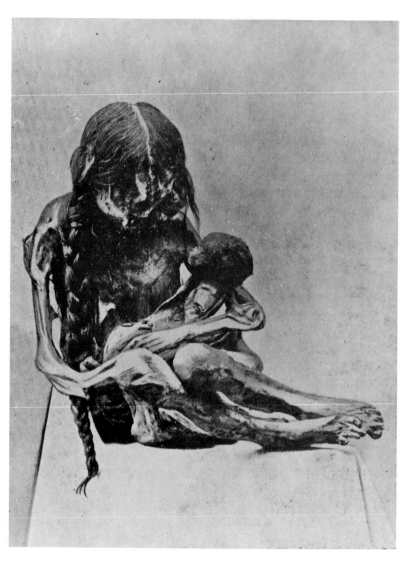

A mummy excavated by Almagro, Chiuchiu, Bolivia, 1864.

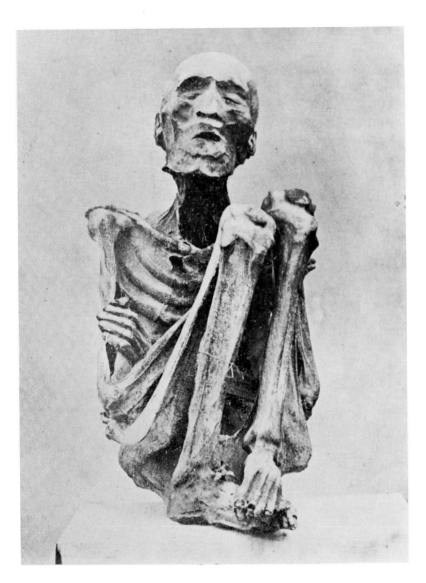

Another mummy found by Almagro in Chiuchiu, 1864.

Cayambe Peak, Ecuador, sketched by Francisco Martínez,
November, 1864.

Chimborazo Peak, Ecuador, sketched by Martínez, November, 1864.

Pichincha Volcano, Ecuador, sketched by Martínez, December, 1864.

Cotopaxi Volcano, Ecuador, sketched by Martínez, December, 1864.

A water-bearer of Quito, Ecuador, January, 1865.

Loreto Indians of the Napo River region, Ecuador, June, 1865.

The customhouse at Pernambuco, Brazil, November, 1865.

The jail at Pernambuco, November, 1865.

Cruz Street in Pernambuco, November, 1865.

dians of the interior. "The Indians dye it mulberry color with some leaves called *sani* and black with *huito* fruit."[18]

One group of primitive Indian carriers came to the Spaniards through their friend, Dr. Villavicencio, who brought them to Quito from the Napo River valley. Dressed in purple homespun cotton shorts and waist-length ponchos, they carried long sticks, bags woven of palm fiber in which they had food, and smaller bags with flint, tinder, needles, tobacco, and *achiote* (*Bixa orellana*) or arnatto seeds for painting their faces. Each woman wore a purple cotton "sack with shoulder straps," which covered her from chest to knees. When Martínez tried to get these Napo Indians to take some of his cargo, they replied that they were tired from their journey and wanted to return home free of burdens so as to arrive there earlier. Some of them were persuaded to carry the bundles, and they were paid in advance at the rate of one to one and a half Ecuadorian pesos a day, plus a little more for food. They carried the cargo in baskets with a tumpline around their foreheads and a strap made of tree bark around their chests. A few traveled with their women and children, some of the latter being only eight years old.[19]

In the midst of hiring Indian carriers and studying the geography of their jungle route, the Spanish naturalists were disheartened by news of events in the war between Spain and Peru. On November 25, 1864, the frigate *Triunfo*, on which they had traveled to America, caught fire and sank while anchored in the Chincha Islands. The accident cut the Spanish fire power in half and reduced Admiral Pinzón's fleet to two ships.[20]

That same month an inter-American congress met in Lima at the invitation of the Peruvian government to consider the Spanish threat to American republics. Representatives from the seven largest Spanish-speaking countries in South America declared they would "unitedly take measures to defend American interests against Spain." At the end of November, Ecuador followed Chile's example by pro-

---

[18] Almagro, *Breve*, 80–81; Martínez, "*Diario*," Dec. 27, 1864, AMCN.

[19] *Ibid.*, Dec. 18, 1864, AMCN.

[20] Davis, *Last Conquistadores*, 118.

hibiting the Spanish squadron from obtaining provisions and fuel in its ports. Meanwhile, Peruvian agents in Quito tried to get Ecuador to declare war on Spain. "Since the seizure of the Chinchas," wrote Isern, "the Hispano-American republics do not look well upon us, the 'Goths' as they call us. They say that the commission has come here to make a survey and draw maps. . . . I hope that our government will award me a diploma in engineering since my talents have been judged with such generosity."[21]

Morale of the four naturalists, weakened by intestinal disturbances and the hostility of many Latin-Americans, reached a nadir on the eve of their departure for the Amazon. Martínez, ill and confined to bed, received a message from the minister of public works authorizing the commission to terminate the expedition and return immediately to Spain, but by a different route. They were requested to backtrack to Guayaquil, then proceed home by commercial ship, arriving not later than May of the same year. The communiqué contained no words of gratitude about the work accomplished or shipments of natural history objects received in Madrid. Unhappy about the orders from Spain, Martínez and his colleagues concluded that it was too late to reverse their course.[22]

In February, 1865, having sent most of their baggage on ahead, the four naturalists departed from Quito headed for the jungle of eastern Ecuador. Feeling a sense of changed destiny, Almagro wrote, "We began our march to the east and abandoned the confines of civilization to enter savage territory."[23]

[21] Isern letter VI; Davis, *Last Conquistadores*, 116–17; see also Robert W. Frazer, "The Role of the Lima Congress, 1864–1865, in the Development of Pan-Americanism," *Hispanic Amer. Hist. Review*, Vol. XXIX, No. 3 (Aug., 1949), 319–48.

[22] Barreiro, *Historia*, 277.

[23] Almagro, *Breve*, 84.

# XIV

# To the Jungle of Eastern Ecuador

From the elevated capital of Ecuador to the low-lying tropical rain forest in the Amazon Basin the Spaniards had to cross another cordillera of the Andes Mountains, then proceed along miserable trails from one village to another. Constant rainfall, saturated humidity, insects, and dysentery molested them, but they were overjoyed by the rich plant and animal life, much of it unknown to the rest of the world. Living with savage Indians while observing their folklore and customs was an unforgettable experience recorded day by day in the diaries of the Spanish scientists.

Because of the difficulty of traveling in large groups and of finding accommodations, the men left Quito at different times, agreeing to meet in the village of Baeza in two weeks. Espada and his two Chilean servants, Juan and Pancho, departed on February 18, 1865; Almagro and Isern with their Indians and two dogs left the next day; Martínez with a guide, dogs, and seven Indian porters left on February 24. He had been ill with fever for a month but could not delay his departure any longer. The first day on muleback, each of the men covered the fifteen miles to Tumbaco, passing along cultivated fields of corn and potatoes and a few orchards of fruit trees. Crossing a natural rock bridge, Almagro remarked, "Omnipotent nature, knowing that in this country man would not think or do much in the way of public works, took the initiative to make bridges and other things to aid the poor travelers." In the town of Tumbaco, Espada complained that "ticks, fleas, and bedbugs work nightly against man—mosquitoes by day."[1] Leaving their mules in Tumbaco, the Spaniards picked up Indian carriers for the foot trail to Baeza.

[1] Almagro, *Breve*, 84; Jiménez de la Espada, *Diario*, 159–60; Martínez, "*Diario*," Feb. 19–24, 1865, AMCN.

In a letter to a friend, Almagro reported that some of their Indian porters were released from the local jail, where they were kept to prevent them from deserting. An official advised him to tie up the Indians each night if he did not want to find himself with the cargo abandoned in the middle of the forest. Almagro's letter continues:

> The system of recruiting Indians certainly does not harmonize with republican principles. When the government needs them as carriers, to repair roads, or whatever, it sends an order to the political officials telling them to collect a certain number of them. Since experience has demonstrated that none will voluntarily lend himself to work, the officer surprises them in their shacks, takes them to jail and frequently shackled, they are led to the place requested. . . . Thanks to an order of the government we obtained [twenty-five] Indians by that system; we loaded them with three arrobas [seventy-five pounds] each, paid them thirty reals and two more each for his food for all the trip which for them would be seven days. This pay was splendid compared to what they were accustomed.[2]

Only one of the Indians spoke a little Castilian; their native tongue was Quechua.

Near Tumbaco, Espada examined a pyramid marker at Oyambaro and, not knowing its origin and history, was surprised that no famous names were inscribed on it. Apparently he was unaware that it had been erected a century earlier when the expedition of La Condamine was surveying and making astronomical observations in Ecuador, and was ignorant of the long legal dispute over the wording of the plaque to satisfy both French and Spanish officials. Espada was not impressed by this marker or by the marble slab placed in a Jesuit church in Quito in 1745 which gave measurements of major mountains of Ecuador. "What do these scrupulous measurements matter to the volcanoes?" he asked. "Will they show the same consideration and respect with which I look at them? With a shake they can under-

---

[2] Almagro, *Breve*, 87; more details and number of carriers in Jiménez de la Espada, *Diario*, 172.

mine their summits, lower or raise the altitudes, and change a scalene triangle to an equilateral one."[3]

From Tumbaco to Papallacta was a three-day trip crossing the mountains through snowy Guamani Pass. Wives of the Indian draftees followed the procession for about three miles, then bade farewell with a chorus of lamentations and tears which contrasted with the impassiveness of their men. One of the few persons the party met on the trail was a merchant headed for the jungle with his trade goods, consisting of a dozen dogs "mostly small and ugly." He said they would bring from one to three Ecuadorian pesos in the interior. At regular intervals of about an hour the Indians rested for about five minutes, occasionally mixing a refreshing drink called *pinol*, made from barley flour and water flavored with ginger, cloves, or cinnamon. The naturalists often detoured or stopped to collect specimens or shoot game.[4]

When they made camp, the Indians cut poles, canes, and large leaves, with which they built a shelter against rain and dew. With flint, tinder, and dry charcoal they made a fire, heated water, and ate their meals of toasted corn, barley flour, bean cakes, and *chicha*, a fermented drink made from corn or yuca (*Manihot utilissima*), alternately called manioc and cassava. Nightly they asked the Spaniards for rum and were given the drink in exchange for a promise not to run away. After supper the natives reclined on their beds of leaves and talked over principal events of the day. Martínez said, "Neither fatigue nor lack of food nor humidity and cold kept them from this nightly talk session."[5]

In Papallacta the Indians camped in the open, but the naturalists lodged in the town hall. "This municipal monument was composed of only one room with somewhat fewer weeds than outside; the walls were of boards not close together since a chicken passed easily between

[3] *Ibid.*, 159, 161; the French-Spanish dispute is summarized by Carlos E. Chardón, *Los naturalistas en la América Latina*, 61–64.

[4] Martínez, "*Diario*," Feb. 24, 26, Mar. 2, 1865, AMCN; Almagro, *Breve*, 93.

[5] Martínez, "*Diario*," Feb. 25, Mar. 1, 1865, AMCN; Almagro, *Breve*, 97.

them; the roof was of palm leaves, and there was no furniture for decoration. Only one door without a lock put the city hall in communication with the pretty Papallacta Valley."[6] The town had only about fifteen thatch-roofed houses made of wooden poles driven into the ground, and the population was thirty Indian families totaling about two hundred individuals. Employment was limited to making rough wooden utensils or serving as carriers on the trail between Quito and Baeza. Goods transported from the capital included hardware, jewelry, textiles, and baggage of priests or government officials; products from the jungle area were coffee, cocoa, vanilla, tobacco, copal resin, gold dust, pita fiber for basketry, hammocks from palm fiber, and *jícaras*, or calabash gourds.[7]

Indian folklore interested the Spanish travelers, especially Almagro and Espada. Both of them took notes on customs, legends, and songs like the popular ballads called *yavaries*, sung at weddings and other festive occasions. An official of Papallacta told them that when a local marriage took place, the guests put the couple to bed, removed their clothing and put it in a pile, entrusting an Indian to watch it. Then they danced around the pile of clothes chanting a long exhortation of advice to the newlyweds on fulfilling their most minute obligations. Their clothing was not returned until friends and relatives donated food, drink, and money.[8]

Death ceremonies were also recorded. When an Indian of Papallacta died, a close relative or friend represented the deceased, assumed the name of *aya*, or "dead one," and took over his property. Gathering relatives and friends together, he proceeded to gamble away all the possessions in a game resembling craps, in which a marked bone was tossed into the air. While the men gambled, the women sat in a corner weeping and relating the life and deeds of the departed one. Feasting and drinking followed the gaming session. In order to compensate the heirs one of the Indians, dressed in cat skins

[6] *Ibid.*

[7] Martínez, *"Diario,"* Feb. 26–27, 1865, AMCN.

[8] Jiménez de la Espada, *Diario*, 155–56. Espada presented a paper at the 1881 Congress of Americanists, *"Colección de Yaravies o melodías quiteñas," Actas del Cong. de Americanistas*, II (Madrid, 1883).

and accompanied by four others with their hands loosely tied, went from one house to another seizing anything they wished to carry away. Objects thus taken could not be recovered by the owners.[9]

At harvest time the Indians of Papallacta sang while reaping their crops. A leader carried the melody, and the other workers followed him, forming a chorus. To fall behind or lose track of the words or melody was a great dishonor, but those who were able to keep up with the leader were praised and rewarded. This system seemed to stimulate the Indians to reap the field in a short time. Another local custom was verse improvisation while drinking *chicha* or something stronger. One would start by making up a few rhymed lines; then the next man would have to reply or continue in the same way. If he could not, he had to pay for all the drinks. Espada was told that this sometimes continued for an entire day with the other Indians paying to hear the poets, for they wanted to make fun of the one who lost.[10]

The Spaniards found the four-day trail from Papallacta to Baeza much more difficult than they had anticipated. Even getting under way was a problem, since a fiesta was in progress and the natives did not want to leave. Martínez wrote, "The Indian bearers were half-drunk, and the guide, Carvajal, more so. We had to threaten them and even use a stick on some to get them started."[11] The trail wound through a thick forest with thorny shrubbery on each side which pricked their arms and legs. Sometimes they had to get down on hands and knees to pass through the thicket. Other obstacles were fallen trees and bluffs to hurdle. It rained constantly. They were soaked with the water that trickled through the leaves, and they had to walk in slippery mud up to their ankles. Some streams they waded in waist-high water. They crossed others on fallen trees or primitive spans constructed by the Indians. Bridges over the Mazpa and Quijos rivers were formed by a ramp on each side made of three tree trunks lashed together and buried in the ground. The projecting ends of the ramps were joined by horizontal poles fastened together. Almagro

---

[9] Jiménez de la Espada, *Diario*, 156.
[10] *Ibid.*, 156–57.
[11] Martínez, "*Diario*," Nov. 1, 1865, AMCN.

said the bridges were flexible, covered with moss, and slippery. The Indians made the sign of the cross before passing over them. The dogs had no difficulty, but the men had tied long ropes on their collars to save them if they fell.[12]

The trail often descended along steep inclines which were dangerous and required much time and ingenuity to traverse. At times the Indians made ladders by notching trees, and each of them carried a long stick with which he helped his companions up and over banks. Estimating the angle of one canyon path at fifty degrees to the horizon, Almagro said, "We fell fifteen or twenty times, and even the Indians with their skill fell—all this in the rain." Another day he remarked, "We have learned that man can have feet of a goat, agility of a monkey, equilibrium of a fish, and the eyes of a bird."[13] At night the Indians cured their scratches and bruises with a mixture of suet and pitch, and the Spaniards soaked their swollen feet and ankles in warm water.

While resting along the banks of the Quijos River, Espada reached into his wallet and brought out a photograph of himself. Showing it to one of the guides, he asked, "What do you think this is?" The Indian removed his hat and replied, "Do you think that we are so primitive, so stupid, that we do not recognize God?" Tempted to give the photo to the man to keep in his house as an object of worship, Espada wrote, "Thus I would be adored for once in my life. But it is not by Indians that I wish to be so loved."[14]

The night before arriving at Baeza was a trying one for Espada. Having sent a man ahead to build a fire and make camp, he saw the column of smoke from the camp site just as it began to get dark. The trail followed a great curve around a canyon, and the Indians insisted on stopping where they were, but Espada continued on alone:

> I had not gone three hundred feet when I found myself at the bottom of a ravine. I tried to get out and find the path, but it was futile; one has no idea of the profound blackness of these forests,

[12] Almagro, *Breve*, 99–103.
[13] *Ibid.*, 98, 103.
[14] Jiménez de la Espada, *Diario*, 166.

above all in this deep place. The fire of my indignation died, and I resigned myself to spending the night there. What a situation, but it was not the first of that kind! I searched for some leaves of that type used to cover shelters and serve as bedding for the traveler, but in vain; there were only two old palm fronds on which I sat down and began to think about the resources with which I had to spend the night. My knapsack contained several things including a towel with which I wrapped my feet, a piece of cloth to cover my head; with my hat under my shoulders and my knapsack as a pillow, I loaded my shotgun with heavy shot, and lighting cigarettes, awaited sleep if it wished to come. I who had eaten dinner became dinner for the mosquitoes . . . I slapped myself raw.[15]

At dawn Espada crawled back to the trail, where he found Isern asleep, and together they went on to Baeza, arriving in midday of February 25.

Baeza, where the naturalists stayed a month recovering their strength and gathering specimens, was a settlement of fifteen people, all related and living in two miserable shacks. Arrival of the foreign visitors brought new life to the town and doubled its size when two new shelters were built. Espada's diary reveals the animation:

Today Martínez, Carvajal, and his followers have arrived; each Indian, thirty in number, came with his dog; they brought four sheep, one goat, and seven or eight hogs. Martínez' two dogs with Carvajal's four, ours, and those of the Indians formed a respectable troop. They attacked everything possible, fought constantly, barked continuously, and made an unbearable uproar at night. Baeza had never been so lively nor with such a population, especially dogs.[16]

The Indian carriers returned to Tumbaco, and others were recruited for the trip from Baeza to Archidona.

Espada was curious about the history of Baeza, knowing that a town of that name and in the same area had been established in the sixteenth century by Egidio Ramírez Dávalos, a captain of the conqueror of Quito. He learned that a gold rush drew many of the

[15] *Ibid.*, 168.
[16] *Ibid.*, 176.

original settlers away to Sevilla de Oro. Then a pestilence took its toll in 1580, followed ten years later by a revolt of the Jívaro Indians which drove the remaining families out. The headman of Baeza, Joaquín Yuga, took Espada to see the remains of stone walls from buildings of the original settlement, about fifteen minutes away from the new one. He said his family had found stone mortars for grinding corn, and other useful objects in the ruins.[17]

During the scientists' stay in Baeza a number of visitors passed through the area. Besides native porters there was an Indian mail carrier who operated on a very irregular schedule (perhaps making the trip ten times a year), the salt man who brought that luxury item from Quito, a witch doctor whose ears were pierced with dangling sticks, and a Spanish missionary priest. Espada watched the native physician cure a patient with a bad leg. Treatment began by blowing tobacco smoke over the sick man, then rubbing his leg with a bundle of nettles. The patient walked away more sprightly than when he arrived. Father Pizarro, the Spanish priest, was on his way to Quito to clarify a dispute in his jungle parish. He supported the Indians in their complaints against forced labor and payments of goods demanded by the governor and other white settlers, stating that his life had been threatened on that account. His compatriots tended to agree with his position, and they certainly enjoyed the chance encounter in the wilds of Ecuador.[18]

The weeks in Baeza were pleasant and profitable, since the climate was mild and the flora and fauna differed from that of the mountains or jungle of South America. Elevation was about six thousand feet, which favored the growing of corn, beans, potatoes, green vegetables, bananas, oranges, and apples. Martínez said the forest was so thick he could not penetrate it except along the few trails or across cultivated areas. To clear patches in the forest, Indian men cut the trees, leaving stumps about three feet high and placing some of the fallen logs around the perimeter. Women sowed the seeds and cultivated the crops, but the men did the harvesting. Rain and humidity made it

[17] *Ibid.*, 184–85.
[18] *Ibid.*, 180, 184, 186–87.

difficult to work and to dry specimens, and the Europeans were bothered by ants, gnats, and a kind of mosquito with a stinging bite that lasted a week. Once Almagro removed fourteen chiggers (*Tunga penetrans*) from Isern's foot; the botanist was in such misery that he had to be carried in a sling by Indians for a few days.[19]

The harvest of scientific specimens near Baeza was bountiful, especially in birds. Espada collected many varieties of hummingbirds, one a diminutive type less than two inches long that seemed more like an insect than a bird. Watching them most of one day, he said their graceful movements had no equal among other birds or butterflies or dragonflies, and lamented that they had to be killed, stuffed with cotton, and placed on a board with a sign reading, "My name is so and so." Probably the most significant discovery was made by Espada when he captured and observed five vampire bats that lived in banana trees near Baeza. Five years later he published a scholarly article about them in a Spanish natural history journal, pointing out that they ate ripe bananas and sucked blood from man and domestic animals. Martínez also commented on these flying mammals, saying, "To keep the vampire bats away one must sleep under a net since they suck blood from the fingertips, nose, etcetera. Dogs and cattle are often attacked, and the worse is that they always bite in the same place as before."[20]

Almost one hundred Indian carriers were needed for the stretch between Baeza and Archidona, where the naturalists would begin the river phase of their return to Spain. The governor of Oriente Province sent a message inviting the Spaniards to stay in his house in Archidona and said he was sending neighboring Tena Indian porters since those of Archidona were victims of a dysentery epidemic. The Tenas spoke Quechua, and had their faces painted with red and black stripes, and carried their food with them: braised bananas and *chicha* or *mazato* made from fermented coconuts. They all had curious nicknames, like

---

[19] *Ibid.*, 180–81; Martínez *"Diario,"* Mar. 24, 1865, AMCN.
[20] *Ibid.*, Mar. 23, 1865, AMCN; Jiménez de la Espada, *Diario*, 181–83, 185–86; Espada's article, *"Observaciones sobre las costumbres de algunos murciélagos,"* *Anales de la Sociedad Española de Hist. Nat.*, II, 98.

Pumasinga (cat nose), Millicuchi (wild pig), or Popacon (red worm). Fascinated by a bellows in the Spaniards' camp, they played with it for hours like children, blowing air at each other. A few of the semi-naked Indians wore garlands of green leaves in their hair and played on reed Panpipes. Espada thought that they resembled characters from Greek mythology. But they were real, and their stamina was amazing, for they made the trip from Archidona in two and a half days, a journey that ordinarily took a week.[21]

For the Spaniards the trip from Baeza to Archidona was more rugged than the previous trails, but they were encouraged by the thought that each step brought them closer to home. Almagro and Isern left Baeza at the end of March, Espada on April 3, and Martínez on April 20 (having been delayed by waiting for more Indian carriers). There were several rivers to cross. The largest was Cozanga, 140 yards wide, which they waded in chest-high water, hanging on to the belts of the native guides. To make campfires, the Indians used wood from the *nina-caspi* tree, which burned perfectly although wet, an important quality in humid forests. Martínez noted that the trail was "unmarked and uncared for; neither the Indians nor the governors want anyone to come and intervene in their operations."[22]

The naturalists remained in the town of Archidona on the Misahualli River until May 10, lodged in the house of the non-Indian provincial governor, José María Cárdenas. In addition to the governor's residence, which was also his office, and a church, there were about fifty shacks in the Indian settlement. Twice a day the natives came to salute Cárdenas, the group headed by the Indian governor, chiefs, and twelve judges, all of whom carried silver or brass batons of authority. Martínez reported, "It is the custom to greet the governor morning and night bringing him food which he might need: chicken, eggs, bananas, *yuca*, *chicha*; other things he gets from

---

[21] Almagro, *Breve*, 107–108; Jiménez de la Espada, *Diario*, 176–78, 180, 185–88.

[22] Martínez, "*Diario*," Apr. 3, 20, May 4, 1865, AMCN; Almagro, *Breve*, 109.

Quito via the monthly mail."[23] Local beer was made from palm tree fruit. The Indians distilled rum from sugar cane or bananas and made another alcoholic drink, pulque, from sap of the agave cactus.

From Governor Cárdenas the visitors learned about Oriente Province, which comprised all of Ecuador's territory east of the Andes. Most of this vast area of more than 50,000 square miles lying at elevations from 500 to 1,500 feet above sea level drains toward the Amazon and its tributaries. The weather was hot and humid, with temperatures rising as one approached the Amazon. From May to November torrential rains inundated much of the land. Oriente's plant resources were abundant: timber, rubber, cinnamon, *tagua* nuts, coconuts, vanilla, yuca, bananas, and many useful fibers and drug plants. In addition to a wide variety of birds, the animals included monkeys, panthers, wild boars (*javalí*), tapirs which grew to the size of a burro, turtles, and boa constrictors. Gold nuggets were washed in several rivers; in fact, Espada mentioned finding a small one in the bottom of his coffee cup one morning.[24]

Indians of Oriente Province were primitive hunters and gatherers. Most of them led nomadic lives, following the ripening of fruits or the migration of animals. Those who were sedentary lived in towns of about thirty shacks made from cane and leaves. Among the most savage were the Jívaro tribe who used poison darts and shrank human heads. Other tribes had been "civilized" by Spanish missionaries, but, as Almagro noted, "Although they are called Christians, they do not have the least idea of Christianity and barely conceive of a Supreme Being. They are highly superstitious and believe in reincarnation—those that have been good become beautiful birds; the evil ones are changed to vile reptiles."[25]

Perhaps the reason more Indians did not adapt to town life was the demand on their time made by non-Indian officials who lived

[23] Martínez, "*Diario,*" Mar. 26, 1865, AMCN.
[24] Jiménez de la Espada, *Diario*, 177; Almagro, *Breve*, 114–19. In 1925, Oriente was split into two provinces.
[25] *Ibid.*, 116.

there. Almagro, substantiated by the Ecuadorian geographer Villa-vicencio, elaborates:

The manner in which commerce is carried on in these towns is highly scandalous. On a certain day the governor and the priest call together all the Indians able to work, men or women; they give each one whether he likes it or not, willy-nilly, some yards of cloth, a machete or knife, and then dismiss them so that in four or five weeks each will bring back gold or so many pounds of *pita* [fiber] at the price set by the amount of goods distributed. Generally five or six yards of cotton cloth were exchanged for one *castellano* [about ⅙ ounce] of gold.[26]

The Spanish naturalists observed other customs of eastern Ecuador firsthand as they visited a number of villages and tribal areas in the Napo River basin.

[26] *Ibid.*, 117.

# XV

# Exploring the Land of Cinnamon

Hostile Indians, debilitating climate, insects, poisonous snakes, and inadequate transportation facilities in the tropical basin between the Napo and Marañón rivers have long kept out European settlers and frustrated the work of missionaries. Called the "Land of Cinnamon" by sixteenth-century Spaniards, much of this area is still as it was then, and its native inhabitants live by hunting with spear and blowgun and gathering plants provided by nature. When the Spanish scientific commission visited the region in 1865, they were shocked by the primitive conditions and impressed by the fecundity and variety of plant life.

The best transportation was by dugout canoes, but this required dependable Indian paddlers familiar with the hazards of rapids or sudden storms and adept at finding food and shelter in the jungle. Language was a barrier since many of the aborigines were never conquered by the Incas and therefore did not speak Quechua. Furthermore, the Indians distrusted Caucasians and were reluctant to leave their own families in order to accompany travelers. But with the help of government officials Martínez and his companions were usually able to get Indian guides and carriers.

On May 10, 1865, near Archidona, Ecuador, the naturalists got aboard native dugouts and headed downstream to Tena. The canoes were about seventeen feet long and three feet wide, and were each made from one tree trunk. It took the Indians about three months to make such a boat. They had to select a proper tree, fell it, carefully burn out the central part, then scrape off all the carbon residue. Sometimes they constructed an arched shelter of woven leaves over part of the craft to protect passengers and cargo, the latter occasionally exceeding three tons, according to Almagro. Dugouts were manned by several Indians: a steersman stayed in the rear to guide with a wide oar, while two or more sat in the prow paddling or poling when necessary. Crew members wore crowns of feathers fastened to a willow hoop, and they laughed and sang while working. It cost the Spaniards one yard of cotton cloth per man daily and one additional yard for rental of the boat. Payments were sometimes made in salt.[1]

All of the naturalists agreed that the canoe trip down the Misahualli River was one of the most enjoyable parts of their entire American expedition. Fresh breezes blew constantly, there were few insects to bother them, and they enjoyed seeing the colorful trees and birds near the shore. The river flowed swiftly over its shallow bottom, submerged trees, rocks, and rapids forming a challenge to navigation. More than once the paddlers had to jump into the water to guide the craft or help it over an obstacle.

Stopping in Tena for a day and a half, the travelers had an opportunity to see the village of about twenty shacks and collect specimens. Excerpts from Espada's diary describe life in a typical house on the river bank:

> The eight-yard-square hut is inhabited by two elderly Indians, two matrons, two young married women with their husbands, two adolescent girls, and six charming children, totaling sixteen persons. Like all the shacks it had two doors which were closed by a type of screen gathered at the top. The doorway is raised a half yard from the ground because of reptiles so that entering is like going through a window. Furniture is simple; on either side of the room under the slopes of the roof are low benches of native *huama* wood which serve as seats and beds; there was a table of the same wood. Hammocks are hung from the ceiling for the infants. When I entered, the oldest man was lying down which is the occupation of these Indians when they are old. The matrons fidgeted about the house; one of the married girls was with her child, the other cooled herself with a fan made of the tail feathers of a mountain bird. The eldest of the girls was busy changing the water in the apparatus where they dis-

---

[1] Jiménez de la Espada, *Diario*, 199–201; Almagro, *Breve*, 120.

tilled banana rum, an industry taught them by a priest named Herrera.[2]

Espada exchanged some trinkets for a container of rum, which he gave to the Indians of his canoe.

Two hours away was the town of Napo on the Napo River, where the voyagers spent six days. Called *Halm-yacu* by the natives, the Napo was about 110 yards wide at the beach near the settlement. Although the village was larger than any of the others in that area, it seemed to be very quiet and the natives less gay than those of other towns. Eleven Canelos Indians arrived in Napo to exchange their surplus weapons and products for gold. Their bodies were dyed black with juice from *huito* fruit, their faces had red lines radiating out from their eyes, and they wore red cotton shorts and a long *cuxma*, or poncho.[3]

At the junction of the Napo and Yunquino rivers a Yankee named George Edwards had established a successful vanilla plantation. He had come in 1855 with other North Americans searching for gold. His companions left, but he remained as a colonist, receiving a land grant from the government. Having personally gathered three or four thousand vanilla plants in the forest and transplanted them to his land, he expected to harvest three thousand pounds of vanilla fruit in three years to be sold in Europe at about ten Ecuadorian pesos a pound. He also grew oranges, pineapples, bananas, tobacco, sugar cane, rice, corn, cassava (manioc or *yuca brava*), and coffee. Although he had two Záparo Indian servants and an elderly native housekeeper, Edwards had cleared his own land, planted it, and cultivated it with his own hands. "What a contrast to the other Whites who have to wait until the Indians bring them *yuca* before they can eat!" was Espada's cogent comment.[4]

Edwards also built his own house and made all his furniture and machines, including a sugar mill, tobacco press, and grinder for making cassava flour. Espada said he was an expert mechanic and scientific

[2] Jiménez de la Espada, *Diario*, 203–204.
[3] *Ibid.*, 206–207; Martínez, "*Diario*," May 13, 1865, AMCN.
[4] Jiménez de la Espada, *Diario*, 209–10; Martínez, "*Diario*," May 14, 1865, AMCN.

agriculturalist but thought he looked rather pallid. Martínez agreed, saying, "He is not healthy; in the long run climate is having an influence on him since Whites constantly get sick here, and all have an unhealthy appearance; also fevers are very common."[5] Some residents of Napo attributed the success of this foreigner to his relationship with the governor, but Espada thought it more probable that the governor owed more to Edwards than the other way around.

Techniques of Napo witch doctors interested the visiting scientists. These clever men lived by exploiting the ignorance and superstitions of the Indians, who believed that most illnesses and pain came from invisible darts thrown by evil wizards. Cures involved extraction of the malignant missiles by a witch doctor, who removed all the patient's clothing and sucked the area where the dart entered the body. Espada learned that there were unscrupulous witch doctors who hid a needle or dart in their mouth, later producing it to show their success, while "others, even more roguish, always treated pretty girls in the forest or along the rivers far away from their families." If the patient recovered, the medicine man was praised, but if not he excused himself by alleging that his power was inferior to that of the wizard who inflicted the trouble.[6]

From Napo the Spaniards proceeded down the river to Aguano, a town of thirty Indian families, arriving there on May 19. Advised to construct two large balsa rafts for the trip to the junction of the Napo and Amazon rivers and finding that it would take about six weeks for them to be built, the four naturalists decided to explore independently before reuniting at the settlement of Coca to continue down the river. Almagro wanted to visit the primitive Jívaro, Záparo, and Canelos Indians to the south; Espada and Isern would go northeast to the "civilized" villages of Santa Rosa, San José, Concepción, and Loreto; and Martínez would go on down the Napo to Santa Rosa and Coca where he would supervise construction of the rafts while collecting fish and insects.[7]

[5] *Ibid.*; Jiménez de la Espada, *Diario*, 210–11.
[6] *Ibid.*, 211–12.
[7] Almagro, *Breve*, 120; Martínez, *"Diario,"* May 21, 1865, AMCN.

Hiring six Aguano Indians as guides and porters, Almagro set out for a five-week excursion among the non-Christian savages. He crossed the Napo and Arajuno rivers, then continued on foot to the small town of Curaray, three days from Aguano. On May 27 he stopped at the shack of an Indian called Domingo who was a *curaca,* or chief, of the Canelos tribe. The house had no walls but a good roof, and Domingo invited them to stay, offering *chicha* and agreeing to sell them two chickens. Almagro said that Indians of this area were reluctant to part with their chickens even though they never ate them. Domingo lived with his wife and nine daughters, all of whom were nude from the waist up, their only adornment being necklaces made of glass beads and monkey teeth. Almagro's description of a supper with Domingo lends color to his trip:

> When it came time to eat, the men grouped at one side, the women at the other; they brought us, in one pottery dish, the morsels of wild pig which constituted the meal. The plate was put on the floor and each of us took with our hands the piece we wished, seasoning it with rock salt and hot pepper sauce before eating it. Some of the Indians did not salt the meat but before putting it in their mouths rubbed their tongues with the common piece of rock salt which everyone used.[8]

After two days as house guests of Domingo, who always had his spear ready, Almagro and his attendants moved on south into the region of the Záparo Indians.

The Záparos had a reputation for being hospitable to travelers. Almagro found them deserving of such fame when he stayed in one of their villages for three days at the end of May. Living in the tropical rain forest between the Napo and Pastaza rivers, these Indians were good hunters with a *bodoquera* (blowgun) and poison darts. They built fine houses, slept in hammocks which they wove from palm fiber, and cultivated small plots of bananas, *yuca brava,* and maize. The men wore a long, sleeveless shirt made of the bark of the *chanchama* tree; their women wore only a girdle about twelve

[8] Almagro, *Breve,* 121–22.

inches wide woven from *chambira* palm leaves. Each man had "as many wives as he could secure." Frequently, they drank an infusion of *yaguasca* liana, an intoxicating drug which produced hallucinations and nervous excitation.[9]

A three-day walk brought Almagro to Sarayacu, a town of 150 Jívaro Indians, on the north bank of the Bobonaza River. Jívaro men wore their hair in one braid, topped by a crown of feathers and beetle wings. Almagro found the people inquisitive and gay in spite of being constantly at war with various enemy tribes. The men always had their spears and shields ready, and near their settlements they constructed hidden traps, usually pits lined with sharpened cane shoots covered with leaves. Their houses were strongly built, having two doors—one for entering and one for departing; but the thatched roofs were often set afire by enemy firebrands. Neither Incas nor Spaniards had been able to subdue the Jívaros, nor had Christian missionaries succeeded in changing their ways.[10]

The Jívaro custom of shrinking enemy heads interested Almagro, as it has most Europeans. He found that the valiant warriors used this tsantsa as a status symbol and fetish to assure family and tribe good luck, fertile fields, and victory over enemies. After decapitating the victim, they carefully removed the skin and hair from the skull, immersing the former in boiling water mixed with herbs used as a preservative. Then they fitted the scalp over very hot round stones, each time using a smaller one, the last one being the size of an orange. Finally they laced the lips with thread, making three stitches in each lip. Heat from the stones turned the skin a black color. As might be expected, the taking of enemy heads was followed by a week-long fiesta with abundant food, fermented drink, dancing, and eulogies for the new heroes.[11]

Having spent five days in Sarayacu, Almagro continued up the Bobonaza River toward the town of Canelos, named for the cinnamon trees near by. He chartered a dugout for his group, paying in

[9] *Ibid.*, 119.
[10] *Ibid.*, 119, 122.
[11] *Ibid.*, 122; Jiménez de la Espada, *Diario*, 207; Barreiro, *Historia*, 339–41.

cloth. They reached Canelos on June 10, but for some reason the town was completely abandoned, perhaps because of an epidemic. This circumstance caused all but one of his six Aguano Indian aides to drop their bundles and disappear. Faced with the impossibility of carrying the cargo and not wanting to abandon it, Almagro sent his lone companion back to Aguano with orders to return with more Indian carriers. Meanwhile, he camped in an abandoned wooden building, burning the boards to roast bananas and birds which he obtained in the adjacent forest. Two weeks later his servant returned with the necessary men, and they all headed back toward Aguano.[12]

Almagro and his party joined a group of Indians who were fishing in a most unusual way in the Curaray River. Their system was to dam off part of the river, then poison or stun the fish with a plant (*Verbascum*) toxic to them. Each Indian crushed the roots of the plant between two stones and put it in the water. Almost immediately the immobile fish floated to the surface, where they were easily speared or simply gathered up in a basket. Some of the fish were *zungaros* four feet long. After a big fish feed in Curaray, the surplus was smoked, and Almagro traded two knives and some glass beads for eight pounds of the preserved catch.[13]

Returning to Aguano on June 26, Almagro hired ten Indians to accompany him down the Napo to its junction with the Amazon. They left three days later in four large canoes, planning to rendezvous in Coca with the other members of the scientific commission. Almagro's canoe was heavily loaded with his servant, two Indians, two dogs, equipment, and four *achangas*, or baskets, of *chicha* weighing about one hundred pounds each. When they reached the rapids of Sopay-punta, water and spray entered the craft in such quantity that it quickly sank, leaving the passengers swimming in the river, which was about three hundred yards wide at this point. The wood dugout soon rose to the surface, and even though it was upside down, the men were able to climb aboard, drifting with the current until one of them grabbed a pole and used it to steer them to shore. As a result of

[12] Almagro, *Breve*, 123.
[13] *Ibid.*, 124.

the accident Almagro lost his clothes, bedroll, silverware, and some of his collections, including a Záparo skeleton. Needless to say, the clothes and camping equipment were not replaceable in the jungle. After righting the canoe, Almagro's group continued on to Coca, where they found Martínez making preparations for the raft launching.[14]

Meanwhile, Espada and Isern were studying life north of the Napo River between Aguano and Coca. Governor Cárdenas joined them in some of their visits, which was a great advantage since the Indians always brought him food and he could easily command canoes and cargo carriers. When they arrived in Santa Rosa de Otas on May 21, they found the village of fifty houses almost deserted following a dysentery epidemic. Although there had been no priest in the town for some weeks, a few Indians were praying in the church and some infidel Záparos were lounging on the church steps. Conversing with the governor in Quechua, they told him they did not want to become Christians because then they could only have one wife and they would also be required to support the priest.[15]

After visiting a Záparo village, Espada declared, "There is nothing more dismal and savage than the site where the Záparo of Rumiyacu dwell." Being seminomadic and changing their location frequently, they built simple houses, usually only a lean-to or roofed shack. Portable hammocks served as beds, and their utensils consisted of a few crude pottery bowls, baskets, and gourds. Cassava and bananas were the staple diet, supplemented with fish, crocodiles, monkeys, wild pig, and birds. They did not make any soups or stews but ate everything dry, washed down with fermented *yuca chicha*. For weapons the men relied on spears launched with a spear thrower, blowguns, and poison darts.[16]

Espada spent one night with a Záparo family, sleeping in a hammock in the midst of people, dogs, and domesticated parrots. His hosts undressed and retired at twilight, and he noted that the women's

---

[14] *Ibid.*, 125–27.
[15] Jiménez de la Espada, *Diario*, 216–17.
[16] *Ibid.*, 217–23.

bodies were painted in a design from face to breasts and from navel to ankles. Females wore short hair, earrings, and tight cords around their necks, wrists, and ankles. The men wore long hair. Espada's diary contains a lexicon of Záparo words and clues to their beliefs and customs. In their dualistic religion Mungia was an evil spirit, the black phantom of the forest, who was always lurking there ready to overpower and devour a lonely traveler. For that reason Záparos seldom traveled alone. Occasionally Záparo men used an intoxicating drug made from a vine called *aya-huasco*. This concoction produced dizziness, hallucinations, stimulation of the nervous system, stupor, and, afterward, hangover.[17]

During June of 1865, Espada and Isern traveled separately to the Ecuadorian towns of Cotapino, Concepción, Avila, Loreto, and San José. Most of the Indians in this area were called Christians, but they still practiced many pagan rites. Trails between settlements were as bad as any in the country—rivers had to be crossed by wading or swimming, and local guides were necessary because the roads were unmarked forest paths. Cotapino was being moved to another location on account of an epidemic, and no one was in Concepción when Espada arrived there. His Indian bearers, who feared the empty town as had Almagro's in Canelos, dropped their loads and disappeared into the forest. After two days in the town alone with his servant, Ramírez, and a pet monkey, Espada decided to go on to Loreto, leaving Ramírez with the equipment. Within an hour he was lost, but came across two natives, a brother and sister, who agreed to take him to his destination.[18]

Loreto had about fifty houses, each occupied by many Indians, one of whom led Espada to the shack of the local political chieftain, Aureo Terán. "He was flat in bed with half his body a great ulcer as a consequence of syphilis," said Espada. Governor Cárdenas was supposed to have informed Terán of the Spaniards' visit and sent orders to aid them, but Terán had not heard from the governor. A few days later he did order six Indians to go to Concepción to retrieve Espada's

[17] *Ibid.*, 218, 223; Barreiro, *Historia*, 350–51.
[18] Jiménez de la Espada, *Diario*, 224–28.

equipment. Governor Cárdenas arrived in Loreto on June 7, Isern and his guides the next day. Two days later the Spaniards moved on to San José de Monti, where they stayed at the house of the Indian governor.[19]

San José was higher than other cities of that area, being located on the side of Sumaco, an extinct volcano. Because of its cool climate the natives could raise potatoes, green vegetables, and hogs, which—along with lard—they traded for tropical products or gold. Although the local people were robust and strong, Espada thought they were ugly, especially the men. He also said, "If distrust is a character of Indians, these of San José are the ultimate extreme . . . if you give them money, they count it several times."[20]

Corpus Christi fiesta was in progress when the Spaniards arrived in San José, and it continued for the week they were there. To the music of flutes, rattles, and drums a group of Indians wearing feathered crowns serenaded the governor the first evening. Their wooden drums with monkey-skin heads and vibrating cord were played mostly with the fingers of the left hand; the wind instruments were made from bird bones with six round holes for the fingers and a rectangular one for the sound; and the rattles were seeds in a gourd or hollowed stick. All the instruments were made in the village. The governor sang and danced with them, and the maids of his house brought out many gourds of *chicha* before the revelers moved on to another house.[21]

San José dances were performed either in a circle or more commonly with the men in one line and the women in another facing each other at a distance of about two yards. In the latter form the men, including the musicians, took one and a half steps forward, then the same backward, while their partners gave little jumps back and forth keeping both feet together. Women danced with their heads inclined and hair covering their face and shoulders, infants often tied across their chests with long scarves. For fiestas the Indians painted delicate

[19] *Ibid.*, 229–31.
[20] *Ibid.*, 231–34, 240.
[21] *Ibid.*, 235–42.

zigzag lines from the corners of their mouths to their ears, under their eyes, and on the cheeks in a variety of patterns. The children's chests were also decorated with lines drawn with vegetable dyes.[22]

Next to the governor of San José the most important people were the two stewards chosen each year who had to supervise the many banquets and be hosts at the dances. Following a visit to the two stewards' homes in San José, Espada reported that each had an altar decorated with mirrors, white linens, and cut flowers, but no crucifix or other Christian symbol. At one of the banquets he ate cooked monkey, eggs, and potatoes, noting that "everything they gave me was divided with their teeth or dirty fingers, and I endured all this to be able to say I had eaten with them." He said it was not possible to calculate the quantity of *chicha* an Indian drinks, or the total consumed at such a fiesta. "They never cease serving it, everyone is spotted with it, all smell of it." His final evaluation of the Indian celebration: "The fiesta is reduced to noise, dance, and *chicha*—morning, noon, and night. In this they are seen as a race of children; they like noise and are tireless, impatient, and simple in their desires."[23]

Ten pages of Espada's diary are devoted to his observations of the San José Indian celebration, for he participated in each phase of it. Included are some anecdotes like the following:

> The women, when they were told in jest that I was trying to marry one of them, answered none would want me since I was not a Christian but the devil. Nevertheless, they did not refuse the crosses and pious medals from the hands of that personage; it is very true that women receive what they like most from the devil.[24]

Being experienced and dedicated mountain climbers, Espada and Isern decided to scale Sumaco, which they could see very plainly from San José. The major difficulty was getting Indian guides, since local people feared the winds and spirits that dwelt on the mountain. Finally in mid-June they departed with two men who had to walk

[22] *Ibid.*, 242.
[23] *Ibid.*, 236–39, 243–44.
[24] *Ibid.*, 244–45.

ahead cutting a path through cane thickets, vines, and ferns with machetes. The first evening at a primitive shelter they saw roosters whose larynges had been perforated to keep them from crowing and thus giving away the location to thieves or those who might be seeking supplies. The next day tremendous cloudbursts kept them from reaching the top of the more than two-mile-high mountain, but they were glad they had tried since they passed by beautiful waterfalls and enjoyed the views from the slope.[25]

Returning to Coca on the Napo River, the zoologist and the botanist worked on their collections of specimens gathered in the Napo region. A few items listed by Isern were ferns, nightshades, bellflowers, lianas, passion flowers, canna, palm, exotic fruits, and herbs. Espada made a catalog of hundreds of birds acquired and preserved. On one occasion he cut down a tree and found fifty-three nests, some containing eggs. He also took back to Spain live parrots, monkeys, reptiles, and other jungle animals.[26]

Martínez spent the month of June in and around the village of Coca at the junction of the Coca and Napo rivers. His primary responsibility was to get two balsa rafts constructed and engage some Indians to accompany the Spaniards down the Napo. During that time he also gathered examples of plants, mollusks, and insects along the Napo. His most exciting experience occurred when a large tree suddenly fell on his canoe, breaking it and forcing the occupants into the water. Fortunately, they were near the bank, for Martínez did not know how to swim; in fact, Almagro, who also had a canoe accident, was the only one of the four Spaniards who could swim.[27]

Reunited in Coca early in July, the four naturalists made final preparations for their raft trip. They made mosquito nets for their bedrolls and prepared smoked fish, rice, and other foods. For the twenty-six Indians who agreed to accompany them to the junction of the Napo and the Amazon, toasted corn and *chicha* had to be pre-

[25] *Ibid.*, 246–48.
[26] *Ibid.*, 219; MS *"Catálogo de las aves recogidas por D. Marcos Jiménez de la Espada durante el viaje desde Guayaquil hasta Tabatinga,"* AMCN. AMCN.
[27] Martínez, *"Diario,"* May 24–June 6, 1865, AMCN; Almagro, *Breve*, 126.

pared. Indian women chewed great quantities of yuca, spitting it into leaves placed in baskets where it would ferment. The Indian men made monkey-skin drums as trade items for medicinal herbs, dart poison, and salt which they expected to bring back, and native preparations concluded with a "monumental drunk."[28]

[28] *Ibid.*, 130; Barreiro, *Historia*, 370–71.

# Down the Amazon by Canoe, Raft, and Steamship

Navigating almost three thousand miles down the Napo and Amazon rivers culminated the Spanish naturalists' collecting mission and gave them a new perspective of the immensity of South America. Starting from eastern Ecuador aboard primitive river craft, they headed downstream, passing through hundreds of miles of Ecuador and Peru in that fashion. In Tabatinga at the junction of the Napo and Amazon they boarded a steamship for the trip down to the Atlantic Ocean. At stops along the way they gathered scientific specimens to enrich the natural history museum of Spain.

Departure from Coca, Ecuador, was on July 17 in the curious river squadron composed of two rafts and seven dugout canoes. Each raft was made of eighteen balsa (*Ochroma lagopus*) logs ten inches in diameter, thirty-three feet long, tied together by strong vines. An elevated deck made of bamboo canes stood seven inches above the floating logs, protecting passengers and cargo from waves washing over the raft. A thatched shack on deck served as cabin, and other small structures housed the live animals carried aboard. Martínez and Espada, with eight Indians equipped with paddles, were on one raft; Almagro and Isern, with their crew, on the other.[1]

The canoes, four large and three small ones, were long and narrow, each made from the trunk of one hollowed-out cedar tree (*Cedrela braziliensis*). The large ones were about three feet wide and fifty feet long, pointed at each end, with an arched roof of palm leaves covering half the cockpit. The small canoes carried no cargo and lacked shelters, since they were used for hunting and served as

[1] Almagro, *Breve*, 129. Compare raft design with that in Thor Heyerdahl, *Kon-Tiki: Across the Pacific by Raft*, 83–84.

dinghys. Each day two Indians were sent ahead in these canoes to find game and locate a suitable place to camp at night. Often one of the Spaniards accompanied them to collect monkeys, birds, and other specimens.[2]

Chained to one of the rafts was a box containing the remains of a Záparo Indian who died shortly before the group departed. Almagro, wanting the deceased Indian's skeleton, secretly placed the body in a perforated box so that the current passing through would remove tissue adhering to the bones. One night when the Spaniards were ashore, the box disappeared, along with one of the small canoes. Admitting they knew what was in the box, the Indians said the skeleton had used the canoe in order to escape.[3]

Navigation on the Napo was relatively simple: one just followed the main current. Trees or snags in the river formed the principal hazard, precluding night travel, but the Indian paddlers were skilled in maneuvering the craft around dangerous obstacles in the river. In order to stop the rafts, paddlers in a small canoe raced to shore with a rope about one hundred yards long and tied it to a tree, gradually pulling the craft to land. Campsites were often chosen on one of the many islands in the Napo, for they seemed cooler than the mainland. Raft crews were made up of Loreto, Aguano, and Concepción Indians who never mixed socially and would not even eat together. Having lived on the river, the Aguanos proved to be better sailors and paddlers, while the Loretos were more skillful at hunting.[4]

Foliage was so thick and the land so level that, while under way, the men could see little other than river, sky, and green forest. The Spaniards often took a small canoe to reconnoiter the banks or circumnavigate an island, occasionally bringing back lemons, *guayacates*, bananas, guavas, and other edible fruits. Isern observed a tremendous variety of palms—some with spiny leaves, others like fans; and Martínez continued searching for mollusks and adding to his insect collection. Almagro often went ashore when he caught sight of In-

---

[2] Almagro, *Breve*, 129, 131.

[3] *Ibid.*, 130.

[4] *Ibid.*, 131–32.

dians or signs of human habitation and exchanged trinkets for utensils and costumes.[5]

After a week of floating with the current the expedition came to the confluence of the Aguarico and Napo rivers. The Spaniards explored the smaller river for a few miles, encountering a group of Encabellados Indians on shore who fled at their approach but eventually returned to barter food for mirrors, glass beads, and religious medals. Men of that tribe wore a gown made from tree bark; their women wore only a short grass skirt. Almagro took notes on these Indians and others who lived along the banks of the river: Avigiras, Payaguas, Cotos, Oritus, Yaguas, Mayorunas, Orejones, and Ticunas.[6]

Returning to the Napo, they found that it had suddenly risen, flooding islands and the adjacent forest and making it impossible to hunt and fish. Luckily, the trees near the river were filled with monkeys, which the Loreto Indians killed after knocking them down from the trees with blowguns and poison darts. The wooden projectiles were about seven inches long, their sharp tips painted with a black resinous extract from the juice of plants known as *pani* or *ramo* (*Strychnos toxifera*). In Peru and Ecuador the venom, which caused extreme muscular relaxation in the victims, was usually called *ticuna*, while in Brazil and Venezuela it was known as curare. Meat from animals thus killed could be eaten without any danger, or as Almagro put it, "without the slightest inconvenience."[7]

Near the junction of the Curaray and Napo rivers was a settlement called Tarapoto, where the expedition spent the last four days of July. A group of Quechua-speaking Indians who lived there related the sad tale of their flight from the town of Borja, hundreds of miles to the west. In 1847 bands of savage Huambisa and Jívaro Indians fell on them, destroying the village, killing most of the men, and carrying off a great number of women and girls. Since that time the survivors had wandered about the forests, finally settling at Tarapoto. Before

[5] *Ibid.*, 135.
[6] *Ibid.*, 132–33.
[7] *Ibid.*, 133–34.

returning to their rafts, the Spaniards acquired Indian handicrafts and plants of the region.[8]

Five days of riding with the current brought the flotilla to Mazán, remembered by Almagro as the mosquito capital of the world. "Without having been a victim it is impossible to imagine the quantity of mosquitoes that attacked us as soon as we disembarked. We could not keep our hands still a minute, nor eat, nor do anything."[9] The travelers were bothered at night; and although everyone had mosquito nets, the heat made it impossible to stay under them continually. Primitive Coto Indians lived in the forest adjacent to Mazán; they wore no clothing and had no cultivated fields or fixed residences. They were friendly with the Spaniards, trading poisoned spears and some ear studs two inches in diameter, which were their only adornment, for knives and trinkets.[10]

A trail from Mazán led through the humid forest to the Amazon, about three hours away. Almagro, accompanied by two Indians, took this route, then went by canoe up the Amazon to the two-year-old port of Iquitos. He noted that it was "a Peruvian town which the government of that country wishes to develop, making considerable investments there which probably will not give a favorable result."[11] His judgment was faulty, for Iquitos grew to be one of Peru's largest and most important cities. The anthropologist and his Indian escort then went by canoe down the great river to a place called Destacamento on an island at the junction of the Napo and Amazon. Here they rejoined the raft contingent, making scientific collections in that area from August 9 to 12.

The journey from the confluence of the Napo and Amazon rivers to Tabatinga on the frontier between Peru and Brazil required twelve days with stops in Pevas and Loreto. Near the former the Indian paddlers found over a thousand turtle eggs in fifteen minutes, while the naturalists reaped a rich harvest of mollusks, crustaceans, fish, and

[8] *Ibid.*, 134.
[9] *Ibid.*
[10] *Ibid.*, 135.
[11] *Ibid.*

insects. Other items obtained were curare poison prepared by Orejones Indians, two clay pots, an Indian costume, hammocks, wax, resin, and vanilla and other plants. Loreto was the residence of the Peruvian governor of that district, José María Bernales, who aided the Spaniards and donated to their collections.[12]

Tabatinga, sometimes called Sapurara, was the Brazilian frontier settlement where the Spanish naturalists terminated their raft and canoe voyage. Reaching there on August 24, they soon bade farewell to their Indian companions, who headed back to Ecuador after having accompanied the scientific commission for thirty-eight days. The Indians were rewarded in cloth and trade goods for their excellent service as boatmen, hunters, fishermen, and interpreters.[13]

Brazilian officials explained that the naturalists would have to wait more than three weeks for the steamship down the Amazon to Manaus, since it only made a monthly round trip, leaving Tabatinga about the eighteenth. A connecting river steamer headed up the Amazon each month to Yurimaguas, Peru, on the Huallaga River. In other circumstances the delay would have been a welcome rest and a chance to augment their collections, but Tabatinga lacked food and there were no natives willing to go into the jungle to hunt it. They were all employed as gatherers of rubber from the *Hevea braziliensis* trees near by.[14]

Civilian and military officers of Tabatinga and the twenty-five soldiers of the garrison received their meager supplies of food monthly from Manaus. A small surplus was offered for sale by the military commander for an exorbitant price, including "horrible sausages, stale cookies, and insipid coffee." Agostino Rodríguez de Souza, a Brazilian fiscal agent, often invited the visitors to eat, but they still experienced more hunger than at any time during the expedition. Almagro concluded, "Surely the twenty-eight days we spent in Tabatinga attended by so much misery were the most disagreeable of the entire journey, having lived there some days in complete fast."[15]

[12] *Ibid.*, 136; Barreiro, *Historia*, 389–90.
[13] Almagro, *Breve*, 136–37.
[14] *Ibid.*          [15] *Ibid.*, 137–38.

To make matters worse there were torrential rains, suffocating heat, countless mosquitoes, gnats, horseflies, and other molesting insects at this outpost. The naturalists' tattered clothes rotted, their equipment and collections deteriorated, and their health degenerated. Isern suffered from nausea and was jaundiced, symptoms of the hepatitis that led to his death five months later. Lacking financial resources, they had to buy steerage tickets on the steamer, but at the last moment the Brazilian fiscal agent accepted a letter of credit enabling the Spaniards to travel in a cabin.[16]

On September 18 the Peruvian steamer arrived in Tabatinga, and the next day the Brazilian ship *Icamiaba* anchored in midstream. Officers of the Peruvian ship invited the Spaniards to dine with them and informed them that hostilities between Peru and Spain had ceased early in 1865. They offered to forward gratuitously to Belém a small dugout canoe and other items not accepted for cargo by the Brazilian steamer. At ten o'clock on the night of the nineteenth the naturalists were notified that they could begin loading their cargo of eighty boxes, which they had to do themselves since labor was scarce and so was their money. Almagro reported, "On this day no one invited us to eat; we had not been able to buy any food so we went hungry . . . a situation which lasted to the following day."[17]

Aboard the *Icamiaba* was an expedition of North American scientists headed by Louis Agassiz of Harvard University. The Americans were well dressed, luxuriously equipped, and well financed—a sharp contrast to the Iberian naturalists. Almagro wrote that his group felt humiliated and depressed at this encounter. "We were completely broken down, without clothes, shoeless, with long beards . . . the general state of poor health all around made us look more like beggars than Commissioners of a European government."[18]

Professor Agassiz and his wife later wrote a book about their experiences in Brazil in which they recalled meeting the Spaniards in Tabatinga:

[16] *Ibid.*, 138, 140.
[17] *Ibid.*, 138–39.
[18] *Ibid.*, 140–41.

We found here four members of a Spanish scientific commission, who have been traveling several years in South and Central America, and whose track we have crossed several times without meeting them. They welcomed the arrival of the steamer with delight, having awaited their release at Tabatinga for two or three weeks. The party consisted of Drs. Almagro, Spada [*sic*], Martínez, and Isern. They had just accomplished an adventurous journey, having descended the Napo on a raft, which their large collection of live animals had turned into a sort of Noah's ark. After various risks and exposures they had arrived at Tabatinga, having lost almost all their clothing, except what they wore, by shipwreck. Fortunately, their papers and collections were saved.[19]

After six days of steaming down the great river, they reached the port of Manaus on September 26. Brief stops were made at Omaguas, Huarinhi, and Teffé; Agassiz' group debarked at the last-mentioned settlement. Manaus, situated at the junction of the Negro and Amazon rivers, had about eight thousand to ten thousand residents in 1865, principally Portuguese or a mixture of Guaraní Indian and Portuguese stock. The city was 925 miles upriver from Belém or about halfway between Iquitos, Peru, and the Atlantic Ocean. The steamer from Manaus to Belém departed the night before the Spanish naturalists arrived, and they were obliged to wait two weeks for its return. Meanwhile, they tried to remain incognito because they lacked funds to buy shoes and new clothing. To pay for their food and lodging, they pawned their watches and some gold nuggets acquired on the Napo River.[20]

Finally the steamship arrived in Manaus on October 7, and the naturalists went aboard for the trip to Belém. One of the cargo items was not accepted for shipment; it was a dugout canoe full of live reptiles. After they paid the bill for the many boxes of freight, only enough money remained for steerage-class tickets. Martínez described the accommodations: "Such passengers eat after the officers, boatswain, carpenters, caulkers, machinists, etc., and they eat the left-

---

[19] Louis Agassiz and Elizabeth Cabot Agassiz, *A Journey in Brazil*, 208.
[20] Almagro, *Breve*, 141–43.

overs of their table on the same plates just as they left them. The cabin although novel is not very clean; passengers have to lodge with turtles, bananas, melons, and other items."[21] With brief stops to load and discharge cargo at Serpa, Villa Bella, Óbidos, and Santarém, the steamer reached Belém on October 12.

Although Belém, sometimes called Pará, is the principal port in the Amazon Delta, it lies ninety miles from the ocean on the Pará River. Almagro estimated its population was fifteen thousand, most of whom depended on the commerce of the busy port for their livelihood. Chief exports to Europe and the United States were hides, rubber, lumber, resins, and balsams. At the Spanish consulate in Belém there was only one personal letter for the naturalists—no word or money from officials in Madrid. Six months earlier Martínez had written to the minister of public works requesting that 100,000 reales be sent to them in Belém for payment of their debts and return passage. Comprehending the critical situation of the scientists, Antonio S. Piñeiro, Spanish vice-consul, advanced them money for new clothing, forwarded their many boxes to Spain, and provided them with steamer tickets to Pernambuco, Brazil, where they could get passage to Europe. They left Belém on October 17 and arrived at Pernambuco eight days later.[22]

Expecting to find communications and funds from the Spanish government awaiting them in Pernambuco, the naturalists were again greatly disappointed—no messages and no money. Furthermore, the Spanish vice-consul in that port was not sympathetic and would not help them. Their luck changed with the opportune arrival of the new Spanish minister to Brazil, Juan Blanco del Valle. Hearing that he was in the city, Martínez wrote him a letter explaining their circumstances and asked for 90,000 pesetas. Blanco del Valle met with the group, congratulated them on their accomplishments, and gave them the requested funds. With the money he provided, they repaid the vice-consul in Belém and paid the long overdue wages of the two

[21] Martínez to Juan Blanco del Valle, Pernambuco, Brazil, Oct. 31, 1865, Barreiro, *Historia*, 399.

[22] Almagro, *Breve*, 152–53; Barreiro, *Historia*, 397.

Chilean assistants, Juan and Pancho, who then returned to their country.[23]

Martínez, Espada, and Isern sailed from Pernambuco on November 30 for Lisbon, Portugal, from there taking a train to Madrid, where they arrived late in December, 1865. Isern's home-coming was particularly emotional because of his serious illness and because one of his sons had died while he was gone and another one had been born shortly after he departed. Almagro detoured via Havana, Cuba, for a short visit with his family before proceeding to Madrid, where his young bride awaited him. The four naturalists were reunited in Madrid on January 18, 1866, having been gone from that capital for three and one-half years.[24]

[23] Martínez letter to Blanco del Valle, in *ibid.*, 396–400.
[24] Almagro, *Breve*, 154.

# Back in Spain

JANUARY OF 1866 was a most unfortunate time for the scientific commission to arrive back in Spain. A financial crisis affecting government and private business was so bad that royal properties were sold to raise revenue. Queen Isabella II, surrounded by court favorites, scheming politicians, and ambitious military adventurers, was becoming more unpopular as details of her scandalous private life became public. General Prim, who eventually overthrew the Queen, led a preliminary unsuccessful revolt in Madrid in January, and at the same time there were Carlist uprisings in the Balearic Islands and republican demonstrations in Andalusia. In the middle of the month disturbing news arrived from Spain's Pacific fleet—the schooner *Covadonga* had been captured by the Chilean Navy, and Admiral Pareja, who replaced Admiral Pinzón as commanding officer of the Spanish squadron, had committed suicide aboard the *Resolución*. An ultimatum issued by Pareja led Chile to declare war on Spain in September, 1865; and a few months later, Spain found herself at war with the Quadruple Alliance of Chile, Peru, Ecuador, and Bolivia.[1]

In this somber atmosphere of Spanish domestic and foreign unrest, Juan Isern died on January 23, 1866, a victim of hepatic infection picked up in the Amazon Basin. Saddened and disheartened, Patricio Paz and the remaining three members of the commission attended the funeral, but there was no official homage or recognition of public gratitude for this scientific martyr who died at the age of forty. His

[1] Spanish domestic troubles in Van Aken, *Pan-Hispanism*, 107; Davis, *Last Conquistadores*, 3, 254, 325; war declaration dates, 265. Spanish reaction to capture of *Covadonga* in *La América*, Madrid, Jan. 27, 1866, 2.

widow and children were awarded a pitiful pension of 35 pesetas monthly, later raised to 1,300 annually.[2]

Plans to hold a public exposition of the items brought back to Spain by the commission were formulated early in 1866. Conferences between the director of public instruction and minister of public works, supplemented with suggestions by officials of Madrid's museums, led to a royal decree setting forth Her Catholic Majesty's disposition regarding the scientific expedition. This royal order of March 6 contained the following five points: (1) a public exhibition of the collections was to be held in the galleries of the Botanical Garden beginning in May (the naturalists were to mount the displays); (2) members of the commission were to write a brief popular account of their trip and compile a list of the collections (this work would be published and sold at the exposition); (3) the commissioners were given two years to study and complete a multivolume scientific work pointing out their findings, the tomes to be printed with suitable engravings and illustrations; (4) their salaries would continue (they should render their accounts immediately and not ask for arrears except back salary); (5) the royal council of public instruction would determine any raise in rank offered as recompense to the naturalists for carrying out their mission in America.[3]

During March and April, preparations for the exposition went forward rapidly. Because of the deaths of Amor and Isern, items collected in their fields were installed by university professors and museum curators. Patricio Paz had the help of Professor Joaquín Hidalgo with the mollusk display; Martínez and Espada each had a technical assistant. In addition to setting up his anthropological displays Almagro agreed to write the popular account of the expedition, completing it on May 3 and dedicating the slim book to Marqués

[2] Davis, *Last Conquistadores*, 11, gives Isern's death date as Dec. 23, 1865; Francisco de las Barras de Aragón, *"Los últimos escritores de Indias,"* *Bol. de la Real Soc. Geog.*, Vol. LXXXV (1949), 60, says Jan. 25, 1866; Barreiro, *Historia*, 494, citing Isern's corresp. seems to be correct with Jan. 23, 1866.

[3] Almagro, *Breve*, 3; Barreiro, *Historia*, 404–405; Vega de Armijo to Miguel Colmeiro, June 29, 1866, Colmeiro Corresp., 5 Div., 62–63, JB.

Vega de Armijo, minister of public works. Notations in museum records indicate that 510 copies were sold at the exposition; two years later the museum's director complained that he could not locate a single copy to study.[4]

Many dignitaries and a sizable public crowd attended opening ceremonies of the Exposition of the Pacific on May 15, 1866. The exhibits occupied three large halls and two galleries in the Botanical Garden's main building. Oil portraits of Fernando Amor and Juan Isern were given a prominent position in the principal salon, as were about 170 large prints of photographs made by Castro on the expedition. One of the dugout canoes used by the naturalists on the Napo River received considerable attention from the spectators, who could read on the identification label that it cost eight yards of cotton cloth.[5]

Objects relating to archaeology, anthropology, and ethnology were located in the two galleries at each end of the building. Among outstanding items were 37 mummies taken from Indian burials in America. One was from Chiloé Island, Chile; others from Chiuchiu, Bolivia, and various sites in Peru. Pottery, jewelry, bags of seeds, and artifacts found in the graves were displayed with the mummies. There were also 41 skulls of Guaraní, Araucanian, Aymará, and Inca Indians, of which 18 showed that the foreheads had been deformed in infancy by the use of slant boards. Photographs and drawings of huacas, or burial sites, were hung on the gallery walls along with an assortment of 80 Indian weapons and 250 costumes and adornments. Drums, reed flutes, rattles, and other musical instruments collected in America were also shown, along with such things as a variety of hammocks used by the aborigines.[6]

The geological display was composed of 530 rocks and 796 mineral specimens, each labeled with its scientific and common name and

[4] Copies sold in *legajo* 1866, Paz Graells Corresp., AMCN; lack of copies in *legajo* 1868; book dedication in Almagro, *Breve*, 3, 6. It is curious that one of the maps in Almagro's book shows California as an island, a notion disproved a century earlier.

[5] The portraits now hang in the library of Museo de Ciencias Naturales, Madrid.

[6] Almagro, *Breve*, 173–74. See Appendix B, below, for list of objects displayed.

place of origin. There were diamonds from Brazil, gold nuggets from California and Ecuador, along with silver, mercury, iron, lead, cobalt, nickel, and a chunk of native copper from the Atacama Desert weighing 150 pounds. Other specimens included petrified wood, amethyst, jasper, marble, stalactites, sulphur from Pichincha Volcano, and guano from the Chincha Islands.[7]

Over eight thousand plants, leaves, fruits, seeds, nuts, barks, and wood samples made up the botanical exhibit. One section was composed of medicinal plants like chinchona bark, coca leaves, tobacco, *gualusa* leaves used to make a beverage believed to increase human fertility, and several American balsams. Utilitarian plants included white and yellow cotton fiber used for clothing, bamboo and palm fronds for house construction, *turusani* leaves for dyeing fabrics, *huito* and *achiote* for body paint, lianas for rope, resins for caulking boats, black palm for spear throwers, and curare for poisoning spear tips and darts. Native food plants ranged from cereals to fruits, vegetables, and spices: maize, quinoa, cassava, potatoes, guavas, hot peppers, cinnamon, and many more. Plants used for fermented drinks and hallucinatory infusions were also represented in the exhibit. Of course there were orchids, ferns, mushrooms, and woods used for furniture, carvings, boats, and houses. Three outstanding wood samples were redwood from California, striped rosewood from Argentina, and a section of a *sapurema* tree from Ecuador sixty-seven inches in diameter.[8]

Zoological specimens included mammals, reptiles, birds, fish, and worms. There were monkeys, rats, rabbits, chinchillas, sloths, anteaters, lizards, frogs, crocodiles, bats, snakes, and reptile eggs. Almost 3,500 birds were on display, varying in size from minute hummingbirds to gigantic condors. Unusual types were colorfully plumed toucans, *septicolores* (named for the seven colors of their feathers), white swallows, black-necked swans, partridges, penguins, and the *camiqui*, a curious hen with two spurs on each wing and a horn directly

7 *Ibid.*, 157–58.
8 *"Herbario de la Comisión Científica del Pacífico,"* 5 Div., No. 68, Colmeiro Corresp., JB; Almagro, *Breve*, 159.

over its beak. Eleven birds' nests completed the picture, some of them made from hair, others from vegetable fibers.[9]

Not counting the many examples that arrived in Spain damaged, the fish collection of the expedition numbered over 2,500, belonging to 677 species. To this must be added turtles and amphibians as well as almost 2,000 examples of crabs, shrimp, lobster, and other crustaceans.[10]

Since there was not time to prepare the 20,000 insects and arachnids individually, most of them were displayed in the jars in which they were preserved. On exhibit were lightning bugs, bees, beetles, butterflies, white ants, spiders, scorpions, mites, and several insect nests. There were examples of insects that emit an exquisite fragrance and others that produce a repugnant odor.[11]

More numerous than all the foregoing put together was the magnificent mollusk assemblage totaling almost 40,000. Some were complete with the animal preserved in alcohol, but the majority were simply shells. They were divided into terrestrial and marine types and further subdivided into univalve or bivalve mollusks. This collection has long served as a reference and training aid for Spanish conchologists.[12]

When the public exposition closed the first of July, 1866, it was presumed that the animal collections would be returned to the Museum of Natural Sciences. However, it took fourteen years and many official communiqués to effect the transfer, opposed for so long by certain scientists who were playing politics. Meanwhile, it was decided to split the collections, offering duplicates to various Spanish universities and institutes. A royal order of February 22, 1868, authorized dispersal of the items, and the director of public instruction notified all the educational institutions about the availability of specimens. Some asked for special categories, others received a mixture; but the fruit of the scientific expedition was spread all over Spain.

[9] *Ibid.*, 160, 169, 171–73.
[10] *Ibid.*, 168–71.
[11] *Ibid.*, 167–68.
[12] *Ibid.*, 161–66.

Records show that items were transferred to Barcelona, Seville, Santiago, Granada, Valladolid, Salamanca, Cuenca, Valencia, Avila, Oviedo, Murcia, Badajoz, Guadalajara, and Ciudad Real, as well as the Naval Museum and other entities in Madrid.[13]

In the meantime, members of the commission and their assistants continued to study the Pacific collections. Almagro left Madrid for Cuba on July 13, 1866, taking his extensive notes along, since he was commissioned to write a detailed history of the expedition. Toward that end he received a subvention from the government, but he died twelve years later without having completed his study. His notes have long since disappeared, perhaps because of subsequent civil and foreign wars in Cuba.[14]

Martínez spent five years away from Madrid teaching in Oviedo and Jerez, but he returned in 1872 as a professor of zoology in the central university. He worked on the mollusk collection with Joaquín González Hidalgo. The two men published three monographs by 1872, one of them with colored plates. With Jiménez de la Espada, Martínez founded the Spanish Society of Natural History and published over thirty articles in the journal of that organization, a number of them dealing with observations and collections made on the expedition of the 1860's.[15]

Espada published many monographs based on his dissections and observations in America and the zoological specimens from the expedition. In 1870 he published an article in the *Boletín* of the University of Madrid about fauna of the Upper Amazon region, and five years later his book on American frogs was printed. In one section of the book he corrects previous speculation about the small frog *Rhinoderma darwini*, pointing out that the female lays eggs which the male gathers up and carries in an abdominal cavity until they are expelled

[13] "*Comisión receptora del Pacífico, 1862–1866,*" Paz Graells Corresp., AMCN.

[14] Biographical sketch of Almagro in Barras de Aragón, "*Los últimos escritores de Indias,*" *Bol. de la Real Soc. Geog.*, Madrid, Vol. LXXXIII (1947), 590–601.

[15] Francisco Martínez y Sáez and Joaquín González Hidalgo, *Moluscos del viaje al Pacífico verificado de 1862 a 1865 por una comisión de naturalistas*; partial biblio. in Barreiro, *Historia*, 447–48.

as tadpoles.[16] Many of Espada's articles appear in the journal of the Spanish Society of Natural History. Other men published works on the vertebrates brought back by the expedition, notably Angel Cabrera Latorre, who was especially interested in monkeys.[17]

Professor Ignacio Bolívar scrutinized the insect and spider collection of 20,000 specimens, publishing a book and several articles on his discoveries of new genera and species.[18] An Italian professor, Daniel Rosa, studied the American worms preserved by the expedition, finding two new species, which he described in the *Anales* of the Spanish Society of Natural History in 1895.

Studies of the anthropological artifacts and human remains collected by Almagro have continued to the present time. For example, a doctoral dissertation was based on a careful examination of the Indian skulls and their deformations; other studies have been published on the mummies of Peru and Bolivia.[19] Countless students have examined the Indian weapons and costumes in the various museums of Spain, each item with its card identifying it as coming from the Scientific Commission of the Pacific.

The story of the scientific expedition of 1862–66 should not be terminated without an evaluation of its significance and some general conclusions. From its inception the commission suffered because it was the creature of government officials in a rapidly changing political situation. Further difficulties stemmed from Spain's financial chaos and aggressive foreign policy in the 1860's. It was a mistake to attach the scientists to a naval squadron whose officers were unsympathetic and bellicose, as the naturalists themselves recognized. Almagro cautioned, "If some day the Spanish government is again disposed to send an expedition outside the peninsula, it will be very much better

[16] *Vertebrados del viaje al Pacífico verificado de 1862 a 1865 por una comisión de naturalistas. Batricios.* Biblio. of Espada in *Bol. de la Real Soc. Geog.,* Vol. XL (1898), *suplemento,* 25–32.

[17] Cabrera Latorre, *Mamíferos del viaje al Pacífico.*

[18] *Artrópodos del viaje al Pacífico. Insectos neurópteros y ortópteros.*

[19] Luis Hoyos y Sáinz' diss. pub. in *Actas y Memorias, Soc. Esp. de Antropología, Etnografía, y Prehistoria,* II (1923), 151–87, III (1924), 1–37, 185–230.

that it not go subject to the plans or necessities of the war fleet, but alone, independent for all that is related to scientific work."[20] It is also apparent that lack of planning led to frustration, duplication, and waste of money and manpower.

But in spite of limitations and shortcomings, the Spanish naturalists covered thousands of miles of America, scorning dangers and illness, difficulties and fatigue. With bold tenacity they scaled Andean peaks, descended mine shafts, and penetrated desert, forest, and jungle, observing, analyzing, collecting, and writing. Although they did not postulate any fundamental theories on the basis of their observations, they did indeed discover and publicize new genera and species of flora and fauna. In addition, they made contact with leading scientists in Latin America, exchanging ideas, data, and specimens. Even the achievement of exposing almost three hundred glass-plate negatives in a number of Latin-American countries more than a century ago was a considerable undertaking worthy of recognition. And what other group of scientists in Latin America met with the emperor of Brazil and the presidents of six republics during the course of their expedition? Or which other one crossed the continent of South America at two different latitudes, gathering plants and animals along the way?

The impressive and numerous collections of the expedition certainly justify its having been sent out and are proof of the diligence of its members. Scientific treasures are difficult to evaluate. The copper nugget, white ants, stuffed ostriches, *ombú* saplings, and Inca mummies have more than intrinsic value. For more than a century the shells, plants, rocks, minerals, birds, fish, mammals, reptiles, insects, and Indian artifacts have been available and utilized by European students and teachers. Many of the items also have been on display to the general public in the museums and botanical gardens of Spain.

If the ultimate test of any expedition is whether its goals were achieved, the Scientific Commission of the Pacific must be considered an outstanding success. Sent to America to collect specimens for Spanish institutions, the naturalists of this group shipped back over eighty

[20] Almagro, *Breve*, 72.

thousand items, each identified as to provenance and many classified with scientific as well as local names. It seems clear that the expedition has been slighted by history, not because of its limited accomplishments, but because of political turmoil in Spain and the premature deaths of participating scientists.

# Appendix A: Regulations of the Commission

ARTICLE 1. The purpose of the Commission is to conduct investigations and observations in the diverse branches of natural science, as well as the acquisition of examples, copies, and drawings of unusual natural phenomena found in the regions through which the escort squadron will pass.

ARTICLE 2. The Commission will be composed of a president [Paz], a naturalist [Amor], two assistant naturalists—first and second [Martínez and Jiménez de la Espada], a person in charge of anthropological and ethnographic studies [Almagro], a botanist collector [Isern], an anatomist [Puig], and a photographer-artist [Castro].

ARTICLE 3. The Commission is divided into scientific and auxiliary personnel. The first category includes the naturalist, the assistants, and the person in charge of anthropological studies; in the second are the botanist collector, the anatomist, and the artist-photographer.

ARTICLE 4. In the absence or illness of the president others among the scientific personnel will substitute in the order given in the preceding article.

ARTICLE 5. The scientific personnel will constitute an advisory council of the Commission whose functions will be as follows: (1) To approve expeditions of eight days duration to the interior of countries in whose ports the squadron will anchor. (2) To decide which of the specimens gathered should be returned to the Peninsula. (3) To examine and approve, if they are considered satisfactory, the accounts which the secretary of the Commission will present monthly. (4) To look into the purchase of objects whose value exceeds 1,000 pesetas and all other matters that the president submits for deliberation.

ARTICLE 6. The functions of the president are: (1) To direct the administrative part of the Commission. (2) To put his O.K. on accounts presented monthly by the secretary to the advisory council. (3) To put his O.K. every week in the books, etc., and in the catalogs of specimens forwarded. (4) To organize the expeditions of less than eight days, naming personnel for these as well as for those of longer duration, being able to divide the Commission in two or more groups according to the nature of the terrain and its products, available time, and special circumstances of the members. (5) To take care that each individual of the Commission performs the duties assigned by the regulations, admonishing them in private the first time if they fail, reprimanding them in the presence of the council if they persist, and suspending their salary up to a month, giving notice of this to the council. If none of these measures prove sufficient, to propose that the individual, who by his wayward behavior or failure to comply with his obligations prejudices the success of the Commission, be dismissed from the Commission. In this case he will be disembarked at the first place from which he could most easily return to the Peninsula. The same will be done with anyone who should not continue the journey because of poor health verified by the ship's physician.

ARTICLE 7. The secretary of the Commission has the following obligations: (1) To write the official correspondence in conformity with orders received from the president. (2) To arrange monthly the account of expenses with corresponding documents of verification, having those in charge of each section put their sanction on receipts authorizing purchase of objects belonging to their respective branch. (3) To keep the daily record book of the Commission in which will be carefully noted the work and operations aboard ship, the days of expeditions, the results of these for each individual, special orders given by the president, and compliance or failure by any individual. (4) To keep the book of proceedings of the advisory council which will be authorized with the signature and O.K. of the president.

ARTICLE 8. Although all the members of the advisory council as well as the botanist are obliged to gather specimens of any scientific field, provided they are considered useful to the purpose of the Commission, each individual will especially concern himself with those things pertaining to the section to which he has been assigned.

ARTICLE 9. The naturalist of the Commission will pay attention to all the scientific specimens, and as his specific task make collections of insects, arachnids, minerals, rocks, and fossils.

ARTICLE 10. The first assistant naturalist will take charge of aquatic mammals and reptiles, fish, crustaceans, annelids, mollusks, and zoophytes.

ARTICLE 11. The second assistant [will collect] birds, land mammals, and reptiles.

ARTICLE 12. The person in charge of the anthropological and ethnographic studies will do everything possible in these areas.

ARTICLE 13. The botanist collector will gather items pertaining to the vegetable kingdom, caring for their preparation and preservation.

ARTICLE 14. The anatomist will be occupied in preparing the specimens given him so that they may be preserved; he will heed directions given by the collectors regarding the organs which should be preserved in alcohol or by whatever methods, numbering each specimen in accordance with the catalog of the collector in which there should be data which will be discussed later.

ARTICLE 15. The artist-photographer will illustrate by the means he considers most convenient objects designated by the president, giving preference to those specimens which lose their coloration or are altered by preservation. He will accompany the collectors on their excursions in order to get vistas of mountains, cuts of terrain, aspects of the vegetation, etc.

ARTICLE 16. Each of the individuals charged with collecting will carry a book in which to record excursions made, who accompanied him, and what specimens were collected. He will assign a number to the objects as a group or individually, according to their nature, so that the numbers will form a catalog of items collected. After each number, comments worthy of mention will be noted, such as the common name, any special use made of the item, its coloration, whether it is perishable, its abundance, scarcity, season, etc.

ARTICLE 17. The president will put his O.K. in these books every week if he finds them conforming to what is indicated in the daily record of the Commission, and if contrary to it, he will note any differences found.

ARTICLE 18. Everyone will take care that the packaging will be done in such a way that acquired specimens will not be damaged during shipment, and will prepare a signed list of same to be presented to the president for his approval if he finds it consistent with the specimens sent.

ARTICLE 19. Remittances will be made whenever necessary from points most convenient for the transport of objects to the Peninsula, directing them to this ministry.

VEGA DE ARMIJO
[*Minister of Public Works*]

*Madrid, July 9, 1862*

# Appendix B: Items Sent to Spain . . . 1862-66

| ITEMS | EXAMPLES | SPECIES |
|---|---|---|
| Minerals | 796 | 156 |
| Rocks | 530 | 178 |
| Fossils | 3 | 1 |
| Plants | 8,176 | 2,000 |
| Animals | 302 | 54 |
| Mollusks | 38,755 | 816 |
| Insects | 23,422 | 4,442 |
| Crustaceans | 1,874 | 179 |
| Worms | 60 | 26 |
| Fish | 2,540 | 677 |
| Reptiles | 687 | 150 |
| Amphibians | 786 | 139 |
| Amphibian eggs | 49 | 12 |
| Birds | 3,478 | 1,117 |
| Bird eggs | 249 | 84 |
| Bird nests | 11 | 5 |
| Mammals | 249 | 88 |
| | Total | 10,124 |
| Mummies | 37 | |
| Grave artifacts | 74 | |
| Skulls | 41 | |
| Hammocks | 11 | |
| Indian adornments | 250 | |
| Weapons | 80 | |
| Drums | 3 | |
| Canoes | 2 | |
| Total | 82,465 | |

# Bibliography

## I. Manuscripts

Archivo del Museo de Ciencias Naturales, Madrid

"*Catálogo de las aves recogidas por D. Marcos Jiménez de la Espada durante el viaje desde Guayaquil hasta Tabatinga . . . 1864 a 1865.*"

Collection of 140 photographs exposed in America by Rafael Castro y Ordóñez.

"*Diario*" of Francisco de Paula Martínez y Sáez.

"*Notas sobre mamíferos y reptiles recogidos por D. Marcos Jiménez de la Espada.*"

Mariano Paz Graells Correspondence:

Box labeled "*Comisión receptora del Pacífico, 1862–1866.*"

Box labeled "Jiménez de la Espada."

*Legajo* 1865, List of items sent to Spain by Commission.

*Legajo* 1866, List of items sent to Spain by Commission.

*Legajo* 1868, *Cartas re instancia de José Mudarra, fotógrafo.*

Jardín Botánico, Madrid

Miguel Colmeiro Correspondence, 5 Div., Nos. 26, 60–71.

"*Colecciones anexas al herbario de la expedición científica al Pacífico.*"

"*Herbario de la Comisión Científica del Pacífico.*"

Museo Naval, Madrid

MS 808, "*Diario de navegación de la fragata* Resolución."

MS 808, "*Diario de operaciones de la fragata* Resolución."

MS 844, "*Islas Chinchas: Informe Escuadra Pacífico, 1864.*"

Photographs of frigates *Resolución, Triunfo,* and engraving of schooner *Covadonga.*

## II. Published Letters

Manuel Almagro to [a friend], Baeza, Ecuador, Mar. 10, 1865, in Almagro's book: *Breve descripción*, 84–106.

Fernando Amor to Laureano Pérez Arcas, Desterro, Sta. Catarina Is., Brazil, Nov. 17, 1862, excerpts in Barreiro, *Historia*, 438–39.

Marcos Jiménez de la Espada to Mariano Paz Graells, Cádiz, July 30, 1862, Barreiro, *Historia*, 501–508.

———. to Mariano Paz Graells, Rio de Janeiro, Brazil, Nov. 2, 1862, in Marcos Jiménez de la Espada, *Diario*, 10–11.

———. to Mariano Paz Graells, Santiago de Chile, April 10, 1863, Jiménez de la Espada, *Diario*, 98–100.

Juan Isern to Felix Borrell y Font, Lima, Peru, Aug. 28, 1863, *El Pabellón Médico*, III, No. 113, 451–52.

———. to Felix Borrell y Font, Lima, Peru, Nov. 29, 1863, *El Pabellón Médico*, IV, No. 125, 26–27.

———. to family, Lima, Peru, Dec. 30, 1863, Barreiro, *Historia*, 209.

———. to family, Valparaíso, Chile, May 16, 1864, *Bol. de la Real Soc. Geog.*, Vol. LXXXV (1949), 69.

———. to Mariano Paz Graells, La Paz, Bolivia, June 30, 1863, Barreiro, *Historia*, 178.

———. to Mariano Paz Graells, Quito, Ecuador, Jan. 3, 1865, Barreiro, *Historia*, 249–50, 271–72, 278.

———. to Laureano Pérez Arcas, Quito, Ecuador, Jan. 21, 1865, Barreiro, *Historia*, 491–93.

———. to Laureano Pérez Arcas, Madrid, Spain, Jan. 4, 1866, Barreiro, *Historia*, 493.

Francisco Martínez to Laureano Pérez Arcas, Desterro, Sta. Catarina Is., Brazil, Nov. 18, 1862, Barreiro, *Historia*, 441–43.

———. to Juan Blanco del Valle, Pernambuco, Brazil, Oct. 31, 1865, Barreiro, *Historia*, 396–400.

## III. Newspapers

Madrid, Spain
*El Pabellón Médico*

*Gaceta de Madrid*
*La América*
*La España*
*La Voz*
Lima, Peru
*El Comercio*
*El Mercurio*
Valparaíso, Chile
*El Mercurio*

### IV. Books and Articles

Agassiz, Louis, and Elizabeth Cabot Agassiz. *A Journey in Brazil.* Boston, 1895.

Almagro, Manuel de. *Breve descripción de los viajes hechos en América por la Comisión científica enviada por S.M.C. durante los años 1862 a 1866.* Madrid, 1866.

Amunátegui, Miguel Luis, ed. *El diario de la* Covadonga. Santiago, Chile, 1902.

Barras de Aragón, Francisco de las. *"Los últimos escritores de Indias,"* *Boletín de la Real Sociedad Geográfica,* Vol. LXXXIII (1947), 590–601, 607–14; Vol. LXXXV (1949), 60–83, 191–99. Also pub. separately, Madrid, 1949.

Barreiro, Augustín Jesús. *Biografía de D. Marcos Jiménez de la Espada, 1831–1898.* Madrid, 1927.

———. *Historia de la Comisión Científica del Pacífico, 1862 a 1865.* Madrid, 1926.

Bates, Henry Walter. *The Naturalist on the River Amazons.* 2 vols., London, 1863.

Bécker, Jerónimo. *Historia de las relaciones exteriores de España durante el siglo XIX.* II. Madrid, 1924.

Bolívar, Ignacio. *Artrópodos del viaje al Pacífico. Insectos neurópteros y ortópteros.* Madrid, 1884.

Cabrera Latorre, Angel. *Mamíferos del viaje al Pacífico.* Madrid, 1917.

Cánovas del Castillo, Antonio de. *Historia general de España.* 6 vols. Madrid, 1890–96.

Chardón, Carlos E. *Los naturalistas en la América Latina*. Ciudad Trujillo, 1949.

Cobo, Bernabé. *Historia del Nuevo Mundo*. (Ed. by Marcos Jiménez de la Espada.) 4 vols. Seville, 1890–93.

Couto, José de. *Cuestiones de Méjico, Venezuela y América en general*. Madrid, 1861.

Davis, William Columbus. *The Last Conquistadores: The Spanish Intervention in Peru and Chile, 1863–1866*. Athens, Ga., 1950.

Díaz de Iraola, Gonzalo. *La vuelta al mundo de la expedición de la vacuna*. Seville, 1948.

Edwards Bello, Joaquín. *El bombardeo de Valparaíso y su época*. Santiago, Chile, 1934.

*Enciclopedia universal ilustrada Europea-Americana*. IV, XXVIII, XLII (articles on Almagro, Isern, Jiménez de la Espada, and Paz). Barcelona, 1908–30.

*Encyclopaedia Britannica*. III, 815 (article on Bolivia). Chicago, 1950.

Esteban-Infantes y Martín, Emilio. *Expediciones españolas; siglo XIX*. Madrid, 1949.

Farquhar, Francis P. "California Big Trees," *The American West*. Vol. II, No. 3 (1965), 58–64.

Fernández Duro, Cesáreo. *El Doctor D. Marcos Jiménez de la Espada, naturalista, geógrafo é historiador; necrología*. Madrid, 1898.

Frazer, Robert W. "The Role of the Lima Congress, 1864–1865, in the Development of Pan-Americanism," *Hispanic American Historical Review*, Vol. XXIX, No. 3 (1949), 319–48.

Gilbert, Benjamin. "Welcome to the Czar's Fleet," *California Historical Society Quarterly*, Vol. XXVI, No. 1 (1947), 13–19.

Gilliss, Lieutenant James, U.S.N. *Observations to Determine the Solar Parallax* (Vol. III of *U.S. Naval Astronomical Expedition to the Southern Hemisphere During the Years 1849–'50–'51–'52*), Washington, 1855.

Gorgoza, J. "*Datos biográficos del profesor D. Fco. de Paula Martí-*

*nez Sáez,"* Boletín de la Sociedad Española de Historia Natural, Vol. VIII (1908), 208.

Haskins, Caryl Parker. *The Amazon; The Life History of a Mighty River.* Garden City, 1943.

Hernández, Francisco. *Nova plantarvm, animalivm et mineralivm mexicanorvm.* Mexico, 1615, and Rome, 1651.

———. *Obras completas.* (Ed. by Germán Somolinos d'Ardois.) 3 vols. Mexico, 1959–60.

Heyerdahl, Thor. *Kon-Tiki: Across the Pacific by Raft.* (Trans. by F. H. Lyon.) Chicago, [1950].

Holstein, Otto. "Chan-Chan: Capital of the Great Chimu," *The Geographical Review,* Vol. XVII (1927), 36–61.

Hoyos y Sáinz, Luis. *"Tesis doctoral sobre los cráneos deformados traídos por la Comisión del Pacífico,"* Actas y Memorias de la Soc. Española de Antropología, Etnografía, y Prehistoria, II (1923), 151–87, III (1924), 1–37, 185–230.

Jiménez de la Espada, Marcos. *"Colección de Yaravíes o melodías quiteñas,"* Actas del Congreso de Americanistas [1881], II, Madrid, 1883.

———. *Diario de la expedición al Pacífico llevado a cabo por una comisión de naturalistas españoles durante los años 1862–1865.* (Ed. by Agustín Jesús Barreiro.) Madrid, 1928.

———. *"Nota biográfica, Patricio María Paz y Membiela,"* Actas de la Sociedad Española de Historia Natural, IV (1875), 24.

———. *"Observaciones sobre las costumbres de algunos murciélagos,"* Anales de la Sociedad Española de Historia Natural, II (Madrid, 1870), 98.

———. *Vertebrados del viaje al Pacífico verificado de 1862 a 1865 por una comisión de naturalistas: Batricios.* Madrid, 1875.

Jones, Tom B. *South America Rediscovered.* Minneapolis, 1949.

La Condamine, Charles Marie de. *Relation abrégée d'un voyage fait dans l'intérieur de l'Amérique Méridionale.* Paris, 1745.

Linnaeus, Carl. *Iter Hispanicum, eller Resa til spanska Länderna uti Europa och America . . . .* Stockholm, 1758.

Martínez y Sáez, Francisco. *El Doctor D. Marcos Jiménez de la Espada, zoólogo y viajero naturalista, nota biográfica.* Madrid, 1898.

Martínez y Sáez, Francisco, and Joaquín González Hidalgo. *Moluscos del viaje al Pacífico verificado de 1862 a 1865 por una comisión de naturalistas.* 3 vols. Madrid, 1869, 1872.

[Mutis, José Celestino]. *Flora de la Real Expedición Botánica del Nuevo Reino de Granada.* Madrid, 1954.

Novo y Colson, Pedro de. *Historia de la guerra de España en el Pacífico.* Madrid, 1882.

———. *Viaje político-científico alrededor del mundo por las corbetas Descubierta y Atrevida.* Madrid, 1885.

Oviedo y Valdés, Gonzalo Fernández de. *Historia general y natural de las Indias, islas y tierrafirme del mar océano,* 4 vols. Madrid, 1851–55.

———. *La historia general de las Indias; primera parte de la historia natural.* Seville, 1535.

Olmedilla y Puig, Joaquín. *Elogio histórico de Don Fernando Amor y Mayor (muerto en la Expedición Científica al Pacífico); Memoria.* Madrid, 1872.

Pons Muzzo, Gustavo. *Historia del conflicto entre el Perú y España, 1864–1866.* Lima, 1966.

Puig de Galup, Bartolomé. *De la moral en el médico.* Madrid, 1853.

Rickett, Harold William. "The Royal Botanical Expedition to New Spain," *Chronica Botanica,* Vol. XI, No. 1 (1947), 1–82.

Rydén, Stig. *Pedro Loefling en Venezuela (1754–1756).* Madrid, 1957.

Sahagún, (Fray) Bernardino. *Florentine Codex: General History of the Things of New Spain.* (Trans. by Charles Dibble and Arthur Anderson.) 11 vols. Santa Fe, N.M., 1950–63.

———. *Historia general de las cosas de Nueva España.* (Ed. by Carlos María Bustamante.) 3 vols. Mexico, 1829–30.

Steele, Arthur Robert. *Flowers for the King; the Expedition of Ruíz and Pavón and the Flora of Peru.* Durham, 1964.

Van Aken, Mark J. *Pan-Hispanism; Its Origin and Development to*

*1866*. (University of California Publications in History, Volume LXIII.) Berkeley, 1959.

Verdoorn, Frans, ed. *Plants and Plant Science in Latin America.* Waltham, Mass., 1945.

Vicuña Mackenna, Benjamín. *Historia de la guerra de Chile con España.* Santiago, Chile, 1883.

Villavicencio, Manuel. *Geografía de la república del Ecuador.* New York, 1858.

Wied-Neuwied, Prinz Maximilian von. *Travels in Brazil in 1815, 1816, and 1817.* London, 1820.

# Index